Geometry and measures

Revised

Statistics and probability

Revised

Contents

Types of numbers

Squares and cubes B2

Square numbers

Any number raised to the **power 2** gives a square number. For example, $6^2 = 6 \times 6 = 36$ (six squared).

Square numbers include:

1	4	9	16	25	36	49	64
(1×1)	(2×2)	(3×3)	(4×4)	(5×5)	(6×6)	(7×7)	(8×8)
81	100	121	144	169	196	225	
(9×9)	(10×10)	(11×11)	(12×12)	(13×13)	(14×14)	(15×15)	

Square numbers can be illustrated by drawing squares:

Cube numbers

Any number raised to the **power 3** gives a cube number. For example, $5^3 = 5 \times 5 \times 5 = 125$ (five cubed).

Cube numbers include:

1	8	27	64	125	1000
$(1 \times 1 \times 1)$	$(2 \times 2 \times 2)$	$(3 \times 3 \times 3)$	$(4 \times 4 \times 4)$	$(5 \times 5 \times 5)$	$(10 \times 10 \times 10)$

Cube numbers can be illustrated by drawing cubes:

💡 *It is important that you recognise square and cube numbers because they often appear in number sequence questions.*

Square roots and cube roots B2

$\sqrt{}$ is the **square root** sign. Taking the square root is the opposite of squaring.

For example, $\sqrt{25} = \pm 5$ since $5^2 = 25$, or $(-5)^2 = 25$

$\sqrt[3]{}$ is the **cube root** sign. Taking the cube root is the opposite of cubing.

For example, $\sqrt[3]{8} = 2$ since $2^3 = 8$

Multiples B2

Multiples are the numbers that appear in multiplication tables.

For example, multiples of 5 are
5, 10, 15, 20, 25, ...

Multiples of 8 are
8, 16, 24, 32, 40, ...

Reciprocals B3

The **reciprocal** of a number $\frac{a}{x}$ is $\frac{x}{a}$ $(= x \div a)$. Multiplying a number by its reciprocal always gives 1. Zero has no reciprocal, because division by zero is not defined.

For example:
- The reciprocal of $\frac{2}{3}$ is $\frac{3}{2}$
- The reciprocal of 4 is $\frac{1}{4}$ (4 is the same as $\frac{4}{1}$)
- To find the reciprocal of $1\frac{2}{3}$, first put it in the form $\frac{a}{x}$ ($1\frac{2}{3} = \frac{5}{3}$), then invert it to give $\frac{3}{5}$

Factors and prime numbers B2

Factors

Factors are whole numbers that **divide exactly** into another number. For example, the factors of 20 are 1, 2, 4, 5, 10, 20. To find all the factors of a number, start at 1 and divide by each whole number in turn. Factors can be split up into factor pairs. For example, for the factors of 20:

```
1  2  3  4  5  6  7  8  9  10 11 12 13 14 15 16 17 18 19 20
```

So, $1 \times 20 = 20$ $2 \times 10 = 20$ $4 \times 5 = 20$

Prime numbers

A prime number is a number that has only two factors, **1 and itself**. Note that 1 is not a prime number.

The prime numbers up to 20 are 2, 3, 5, 7, 11, 13, 17 and 19.

Prime factors B2

Prime factors are factors that are prime. All whole numbers, except prime numbers, can be written as products of their prime factors. For example, the diagram below shows the prime factors of 360:

1. Divide 360 by its first prime factor, 2.
2. Divide 180 by its first prime factor, 2.
3. Keep on going until the final number is prime.
4. As a product of its prime factors, 360 can be written as:
   $2 \times 2 \times 2 \times 3 \times 3 \times 5 = 360$
   or in **index notation** (using powers):
   $2^3 \times 3^2 \times 5 = 360$

Highest common factor (HCF)

The **largest factor** that two numbers have in common is called the **HCF**.

Example

Find the HCF of 84 and 360.

1. Write the numbers as products of their prime factors and ring the common factors.
   $84 = \boxed{2} \times \boxed{2} \times \boxed{3} \times 7$
   $360 = \boxed{2} \times \boxed{2} \times 2 \times \boxed{3} \times 3 \times 5$
2. These give the HCF $= 2 \times 2 \times 3 = 12$

Least common multiple (LCM)

The **LCM** is the lowest number that is a multiple of two or more numbers.

Example

Find the LCM of 6 and 8.

1. Write the numbers as products of their prime factors.
   $8 = 2 \times 2 \times \boxed{2}$
   $6 = \boxed{2} \times 3$
   8 and 6 have a common prime factor of 2. It is only counted once.
2. You take one number from each column, so the LCM of 6 and 8 is $2 \times 2 \times 2 \times 3 = 24$

Quick test

1. List the prime numbers between 10 and 30.
2. Find the HCF and LCM of 24 and 60.
3. Find **a)** $\sqrt{64}$ **b)** $\sqrt[3]{216}$
4. Write down the reciprocals of the following:
   a) $\frac{3}{4}$ **b)** $\frac{x}{p}$ **c)** 5   **d)** $\frac{1}{10}$

Positive & negative numbers

Place value in whole numbers B1 B2

The value of a digit in a whole number depends on its position in the number. This is called its **place value**.

Example

Gill buys some premium bonds for £1050. Write this figure in words.

Place value of digits				Number
1000 Thousands	100 Hundreds	10 Tens	1 Units	
			8	Eight
		7	9	Seventy-nine
	3	4	5	Three hundred and forty-five
6	3	2	9	Six thousand three hundred and twenty-nine

This number is one thousand and fifty pounds.

Directed numbers B2

Directed numbers are numbers that may be **positive** or **negative**. Positive numbers are above zero; negative numbers are below zero.

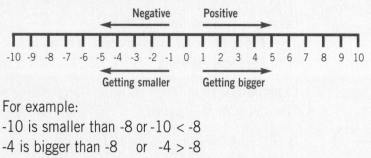

For example:
-10 is smaller than -8 or -10 < -8
-4 is bigger than -8   or   -4 > -8
2 is bigger than -6   or   2 > -6

Directed numbers are often seen on the weather forecast in winter. Quite often the temperature is below 0˚C.

Aberdeen is the coldest place on this forecast map at -8˚C.
London is 6 degrees warmer than Manchester.

Integers are a set of whole numbers {..., -3, -2, -1, 0, 1, 2, 3,...}. They include positive numbers, negative numbers and zero.

Multiplying and dividing directed numbers B1 B2 B3

Multiply and divide directed numbers as normal. Then find the sign for the answer using these rules:

- Two **like** signs (both + or both -) give a positive answer.
- Two **unlike** signs (one + and the other -) give a negative answer.

For example:
-6 × (+4) = -24   -12 ÷ (-3) = 4
-6 × (-3) = 18   20 ÷ (-4) = -5

(+) × (+) = +
(-) × (-) = +
(+) × (-) = -
(-) × (+) = -

(+) ÷ (+) = +
(-) ÷ (-) = +
(+) ÷ (-) = -
(-) ÷ (+) = -

You need to remember the rules of multiplication and division. You will find these laws useful when multiplying out brackets in algebra.

Adding and subtracting directed numbers B1 B2 B3

Number lines can help you to understand the concept of adding and subtracting directed numbers.

The temperature at 6am was -5°C. By 10am it had risen 8 degrees.

So the new temperature was 3°C.

Example
Find the value of -2 – 4.

This represents the **sign** of the number. Start at -2.

-2 – 4

This represents the operation of **subtraction**. Move 4 places to the left.

– 4
Finish ← ⌒⌒⌒ ↘ Start
-6 -5 -4 -3 -2 -1 0 1 2 3 4

So -2 – 4 = -6

💡 *If you find working with directed numbers difficult, sketch a quick number line to help you.*

When the number to be added (or subtracted) is **negative**, the normal direction of movement is **reversed**. For example:

-4 – (-3) is the same as -4 + 3 = -1

The negative changes the **direction**.   Move 3 places to the **right**.

When two + or two – signs are together, these rules are used:

+ (+) → +
– (-) → + } like signs give a **positive**

+ (-) → –
– (+) → – } unlike signs give a **negative**

For example:
-6 + (-2) = -6 – 2 = -8
4 – (-3) = 4 + 3 = 7
-2 – (+6) = -2 – 6 = -8
9 + (-3) = 9 – 3 = 6

Negative numbers on a calculator B1 B3

The [+/–] or [(-)] key on a calculator gives a negative number. For example, to get -6, press
[6] [+/–] or [(-)] [6]

💡 *Make sure you know how to enter negative numbers in your calculator.*

Look at this calculation:
-4 – (-2) = -2

This is keyed in the calculator as follows:

Quick test

❶ If the temperature was -12°C at 2am, and it increased by 15 degrees by 11am, what was the temperature at 11am?

❷ Work out the following, without using a calculator.
- **a)** -2 – (-6)
- **b)** -9 + (-7)
- **c)** -2 × 6
- **d)** -9 + (-3)
- **e)** -20 ÷ (-4)
- **f)** -18 ÷ (-3)
- **g)** 4 – (-3)
- **h)** -7 + (-3)
- **i)** -9 × -4

Working with numbers

Addition and subtraction · B1 · B2 · B3

When you add and subtract integers, line up the place values one on top of the other.

Example

Work out 5263 + 398.

```
 5263
  398 +
 5661
  1 1
```

Line up the numbers first.
Add the units, then the 10s, etc.

The 1 is carried here into the tens column.

This addition can be checked mentally by using **partitioning**. An empty number line can help.

5263 + 400 – 2 = 5661

Subtracting is also known as **finding the difference**.

Example

Find the difference between 2791 and 363.

```
   8 1
 279̸1
  363 –
 2428
```

In the units column, subtracting 3 from 1 won't work, so borrow 10 from the next column. The 9 becomes an 8 and the 1 becomes 11.

Compensation can be used to check the answer, by adding or subtracting too much and then compensating.

2791 – 400 + 37 = 2428

Multiplication and division by 10, 100, 1000 · B1 · B2

To **multiply** by 10, 100, 1000, etc. move the digits one, two, three, etc. places to the left and put in zeros if necessary. For example:

$6.3 \times 10 = 63$ — Move the digits one place to the left.

$47 \times 10 = 470$ — Put in a zero, moving the digits one place to the left.

$17.4 \times 100 = 1740$ — Move the digits two places to the left.

$68 \times 100 = 6800$ — Put in two zeros, moving the digits two places to the left.

When multiplying by multiples of 10 (e.g. 20, 30, 700), the same rules apply, except you multiply the numbers first, then move the digits to the left. For example:

60×30	**or,** 60×30
$= 60 \times 3 \times 10$	$= 6 \times 10 \times 3 \times 10$
$= 180 \times 10 = 1800$	$= 18 \times 100 = 1800$

5.2×20
$= 5.2 \times 2 \times 10$
$= 10.4 \times 10 = 104$

To **divide** by 10, 100, 1000, etc. move the digits one, two, three, etc. places to the right and put in zeros if necessary. For example:

$17.6 \div 10 = 1.76$

$74 \div 100 = 0.74$

$19.6 \div 1000 = 0.0196$

When dividing by multiples of 10, the same rules apply, except you divide the numbers and then move the digits to the right. For example:

$6000 \div 30$
$= 6000 \div 3 \div 10$
$= 2000 \div 10$
$= 200$

$6.3 \div 30$
$= 6.3 \div 3 \div 10$
$= 2.1 \div 10$
$= 0.21$

Long multiplication B2

When you multiply two or more numbers together you are finding the **product**.

Example

A tin of soup costs 64p. Work out the cost of 127 tins of soup.

Cost = 127 × 64

```
  127
   64 ×
  508    ❶ 127 × 4
 1 2
 7620 +  ❷ 127 × 60
 1 4
 8128    ❸ 508 + 7620
 1
```

Cost = 8128p or £81.28

Alternatively, you can use a 'grid' method.

×	100	20	7		
60	6000	1200	420	⟶	7620
4	400	80	28	⟶	508 +
					8128
					1

= £81.28

Long division B2

The following example will help you to understand long division.

Example

A pencil costs 27p. Samuel has £3.66 to spend. What is the maximum number of pencils he can buy? How much change will he have left over?

```
    13
27)366
   27↓ –   ❶ 27 goes into 36 once, put down 1
   96      ❷ Place 27 below 36
   81 –    ❸ Subtract 27 from 36 (get 9)
   15      ❹ Bring down the 6
           ❺ Divide 27 into 96, put down 3
           ❻ 96 – 81 = remainder 15
```

Samuel can buy 13 pencils and he will have 15p left over.

The method of **chunking** can also be used when dividing. Always try to estimate the answer to your division.

```
27)366
   270 –   [27 × 10]
    96
    81 –   [27 × 3]
    15
```

366 ÷ 27 = 10 + 3, remainder 15
         = 13 pencils and 15p left over

Quick test

Answer the following questions, without using a calculator.

❶ a) 479 + 698   **b)** 379 – 147   **c)** 287 × 6   **d)** 5)1375

❷ 427 × 48

❸ 49)1813

❹ a) 16.4 × 10   **b)** 8.9 × 100   **c)** 37 × 1000   **d)** 97 ÷ 1000

❺ The cost of a trip is £15.65. If Ms Kier collects £657.30, how many people are going on the trip?

Fractions

Fractions B1 B2

A fraction is a part of a whole.
The top number is the numerator.
The bottom number is the denominator.

A fraction like $\frac{4}{5}$ is called a **proper fraction** because the **denominator is greater** than the numerator.

A fraction like $\frac{24}{17}$ is called an **improper fraction** because the **numerator is greater** than the denominator.

A number like $2\frac{1}{2}$ is called a **mixed number**.

When expressing one amount as a fraction of another amount, write them as a fraction with the first amount the numerator and the second amount the denominator. For example, 7 as a fraction of 9 is written as $\frac{7}{9}$

Equivalent fractions B1 B2

Equivalent fractions have the same value.
For example:

From the diagrams it can be seen that

$\frac{1}{2} = \frac{2}{4} = \frac{3}{6} = \frac{4}{8}$

They are equivalent fractions. Fractions can be changed to their equivalents by **multiplying** or **dividing** both the numerator and denominator by the same amount.

Examples

a) Change $\frac{5}{7}$ to its equivalent fraction with a denominator of 28.

Multiply the top and bottom by 4. $\frac{5}{7} = \frac{20}{28}$ $\times 4$
So $\frac{5}{7}$ is equivalent to $\frac{20}{28}$

b) Change $\frac{40}{60}$ to its equivalent fraction with a denominator of 3.

Divide the top and bottom by 20. $\frac{40}{60} = \frac{2}{3}$ $\div 20$
So $\frac{40}{60}$ is equivalent to $\frac{2}{3}$
$\frac{40}{60} = \frac{2}{3}$ in its simplest form.

This is known as simplifying the fraction by '**cancelling**'.

Addition and subtraction of fractions B2

These examples show the basic principles of adding and subtracting fractions.

Examples
a) Work out $\frac{1}{8} + \frac{3}{4}$

❶ First make the denominators the same: $\frac{3}{4}$ is **equivalent** to $\frac{6}{8}$
❷ Replace $\frac{3}{4}$ with $\frac{6}{8}$ to make $\frac{1}{8} + \frac{6}{8}$
❸ Add the numerators: $1 + 6 = 7$
Do not add the denominators; the denominator stays the same.
So, $\frac{1}{8} + \frac{6}{8} = \frac{7}{8}$

b) Work out $\frac{9}{12} - \frac{1}{3}$

❶ First make the denominators the same: $\frac{1}{3}$ is equivalent to $\frac{4}{12}$
❷ Replace $\frac{1}{3}$ with $\frac{4}{12}$
❸ Subtract the numerators but **not** the denominators; the denominator stays the same.
So, $\frac{9}{12} - \frac{4}{12} = \frac{5}{12}$
Or, $\frac{9-4}{12} = \frac{5}{12}$

Multiplication and division of fractions `B2` `B3`

When multiplying and dividing fractions, write out whole or mixed numbers as improper fractions before starting. This is an example of multiplication:

$$\frac{2}{9} \times \frac{4}{7} = \frac{2 \times 4}{9 \times 7} = \frac{8}{63}$$

← Multiply numerators together.
← Multiply denominators together.

Change a division into a multiplication by turning the second fraction upside down and multiplying both fractions together; that is, **multiply by the reciprocal**.

Example
Work out $\frac{7}{9} \div \frac{12}{18}$

❶ Take the **reciprocal** of the **second fraction**.
❷ Multiply the fractions as normal.
So, $\frac{7}{9} \times \frac{18}{12} = \frac{126}{108}$
❸ Rewrite the answer as a mixed number.
$\frac{126}{108} = 1\frac{18}{108} = 1\frac{1}{6}$

Using the fraction key on a calculator `B1` `B3`

$a^{b/c}$ is the fraction key on many calculators. For example, 12 out of 18 can be written as $\frac{12}{18}$
$\frac{12}{18}$ is keyed in as [1] [2] [a^b/c] [1] [8]

This is displayed as $12 \lrcorner 18$ or $12 \ulcorner 18$

The calculator will automatically cancel down fractions when the [=] key is pressed.

For example, $\frac{12}{18}$ becomes $2 \lrcorner 3$ or $2 \ulcorner 3$
This means two-thirds.

A display of $1 \lrcorner 4 \lrcorner 9$ means $1\frac{4}{9}$. If you now press [shift] [a^b/c], it converts back to an improper fraction, $13 \lrcorner 9$, which means $\frac{13}{9}$

ⓘ *Make sure you know which is the fraction key on your calculator.*

Proportional changes with fractions `B1` `B2`

Increase and decrease
There are two methods for working out proportional changes with fractions. Use the one that is familiar to you. Remember that 'of' means multiply.

Example
Last year a gym had 290 members. This year there are $\frac{3}{5}$ more. How many members are there now?

Method 1
❶ Work out $\frac{1}{5}$ **of** 290 = 58, so $\frac{3}{5} \times 290 = 174$
❷ Add this to the original number, so
290 + 174 = 464 people

Method 2
Increasing by $\frac{3}{5}$ is the same as multiplying by $1\frac{3}{5}$
$(1 + \frac{3}{5})$.
On the calculator, key in

[1] [a^b/c] [3] [a^b/c] [5] [×] [290] [=]

$1\frac{3}{5} \times 290 = 464$

ⓘ *Make sure you know how to use your calculator to add, subtract, multiply and divide fractions.*

Quick test

❶ Without using a calculator, work out the following:
  a) $\frac{2}{9} + \frac{3}{27}$ b) $\frac{3}{5} - \frac{1}{4}$ c) $\frac{6}{9} \times \frac{72}{104}$ d) $\frac{8}{9} \div \frac{2}{3}$
  e) $\frac{4}{7} - \frac{1}{3}$ f) $\frac{2}{7} \div 1\frac{1}{2}$ g) $\frac{7}{11} \div \frac{22}{14}$ h) $\frac{2}{9} + \frac{4}{7}$

❷ Calculate $\frac{2}{9}$ of £180.

❸ $\frac{7}{12}$ more rain fell this year than last year. If 156mm fell last year, how much rain fell this year? 🖩

❹ A mixed selection of biscuits has $\frac{1}{3}$ chocolate and $\frac{2}{5}$ jam cream biscuits. The rest of the biscuits are plain. What fraction of the biscuits are plain?

Decimals

Types of decimals B2

A **decimal point** is used to separate whole number columns from fractional columns.
For example:

Decimal point

Thousands	Hundreds	Tens	Units			Tenths	Hundredths	Thousandths
8	9	2	4	•		1	6	3

The 1 means $\frac{1}{10}$, the 6 means $\frac{6}{100}$, the 3 means $\frac{3}{1000}$

Terminating and recurring decimals

A decimal that stops is called a terminating decimal. All terminating decimals can be written as a fraction. For example:

$0.273 = \frac{273}{1000}$

$0.49 = \frac{49}{100}$

$0.7 = \frac{7}{10}$

If a fraction written in its simplest form has a denominator with a prime factor other than 2 or 5, it will convert to a recurring decimal. A decimal that recurs is shown by placing a dot over the numbers that repeat. For example:

$0.333... = 0.\dot{3}$

$0.17777... = 0.1\dot{7}$

$0.232323... = 0.\dot{2}\dot{3}$

Multiplying and dividing decimals by 10, 100, 1000 B1 B2

To multiply a decimal number by 10, 100, 1000, etc. move each digit one, two, three, etc. places to the left. For example:

$8.7 \times 10 = 87$

$15.62 \times 10 = 156.2$

$15.27 \times 100 = 1527$

$29.369 \times 1000 = 29369$

To divide decimals by 10, 100, 1000, etc. move each digit one, two, three, etc. places to the right. For example:

$146.2 \div 100 = 1.462$

$27.6 \div 1000 = 0.0276$

Ordering decimals B1 B2

When ordering decimals, follow these steps:
1. First write them with the same number of figures after the decimal point.
2. Then compare whole numbers, digits in the tenths place, digits in the hundredths place, and so on.

💡 *Remember, hundredths are smaller than tenths:* $\frac{10}{100} = \frac{1}{10}$ so $\frac{8}{100} < \frac{1}{10}$

Example
The results below show the distance, in metres, that some students achieved when throwing the discus:
16.21m, 16.02m, 16.4m, 16.04m, 12.71m, 18.3m
Arrange these distances in order of size, smallest first.

1. Rewrite them with two figures after the decimal point: 16.21, 16.02, 16.40, 16.04, 12.71, 18.30
2. Now reorder them:
   12.71, 16.02, 16.04, 16.21, 16.40, 18.30
3. Rewrite them in the original form: 12.71m, 16.02m, 16.04m, 16.21m, 16.4m, 18.3m

Multiplying and dividing by numbers between 0 and 1 B3

When **multiplying** by numbers between 0 and 1, the result is always **smaller** than the starting value.

For example: 6 × 0.1 = 0.6
6 × 0.01 = 0.06
6 × 0.001 = 0.006

The results are all smaller than the starting values.

When **dividing** by numbers between 0 and 1, the result is always **bigger** than the starting value.

For example: 6 ÷ 0.1 = 60
6 ÷ 0.01 = 600
6 ÷ 0.001 = 6000

The results are all bigger than the starting values.

Calculations with decimals B1 B2 B3

When **adding** and **subtracting** decimals, the decimal points need to go under each other. For example:

$$27.46$$
$$7.291 +$$
$$34.751$$

$$1\overset{6}{7}.\overset{9}{0}\overset{1}{0}$$
$$12.84 -$$
$$4.16$$

Line up the digits carefully. Put the decimal points under each other. The decimal point in the answer will then be in line.

💡 *Remember to line up the digits carefully.*

When **multiplying** decimals, the answer must have the same number of decimal places as the total number of decimal places in the numbers that are being multiplied. For example, 84 × 1.4 = 117.6

Examples

a) Work out 24.6 × 7.

$$246$$
$$7 \times$$
$$1722$$

Multiply 246 by 7 = 1722, ignoring the decimal point. 24.6 has 1 number after the decimal point. The answer must have 1 decimal place (1 d.p.).

So 24.6 × 7 = 172.2

b) Work out 4.52 × 0.2

$$452$$
$$2 \times$$
$$904$$

Work out 452 × 2, ignoring the decimal points. 4.52 has 2 d.p.; 0.2 has 1 d.p. So the answer must have 3 d.p.

904 ⟶ 0.904 *Move the digits 3 places to the right.*

So 4.52 × 0.2 = 0.904

When **dividing** decimals, divide as normal, placing the decimal points in line. For example:

$$\begin{array}{r} 4.8 \\ 3\overline{)14.^14} \end{array}$$

Put the decimal points in line.

A fraction can be changed into a decimal by dividing the numerator by the denominator. For example, this is how you would change $\frac{3}{5}$ into a decimal by short division:

$$\begin{array}{r} 0.6 \\ 5\overline{)3.^30} \end{array}$$

When dividing by a decimal, it is easier to multiply the numerator and denominator by a power of 10, so that it becomes equivalent to a division with a whole number. For example:

$$\frac{275}{0.25} = \frac{27\,500}{25}$$

Multiply the numerator and denominator by 100.

$$= 1100$$

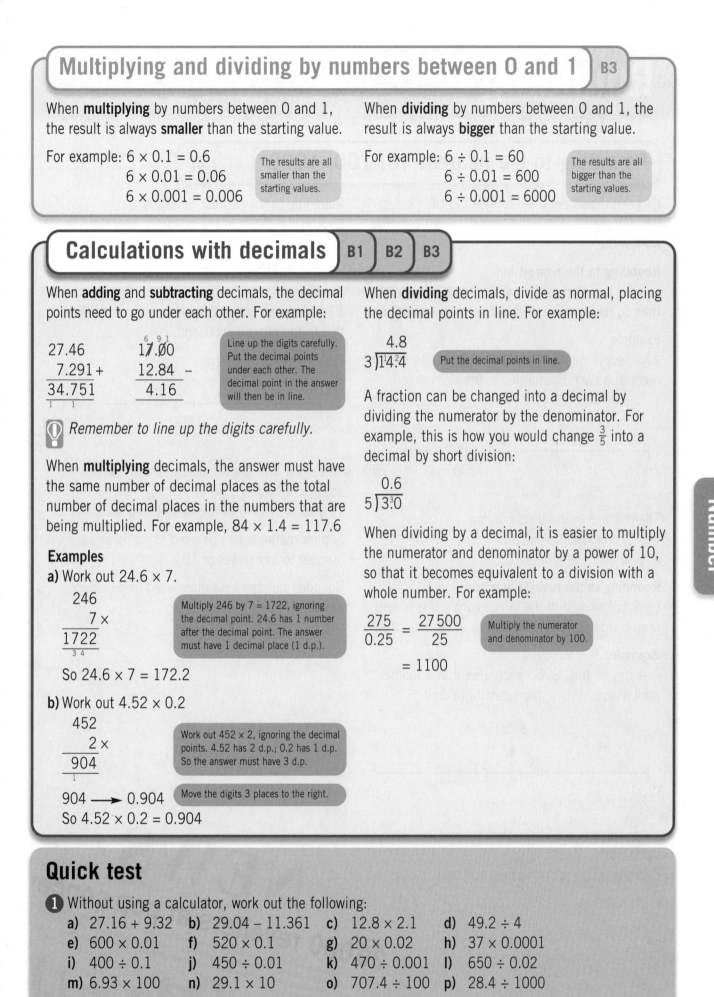

Quick test

1 Without using a calculator, work out the following:
  a) 27.16 + 9.32 b) 29.04 − 11.361 c) 12.8 × 2.1 d) 49.2 ÷ 4
  e) 600 × 0.01 f) 520 × 0.1 g) 20 × 0.02 h) 37 × 0.0001
  i) 400 ÷ 0.1 j) 450 ÷ 0.01 k) 470 ÷ 0.001 l) 650 ÷ 0.02
  m) 6.93 × 100 n) 29.1 × 10 o) 707.4 ÷ 100 p) 28.4 ÷ 1000

2 Arrange these numbers in order of size, smallest first.
  a) 2.61, 4.02, 4.20, 4.021, 2.615, 2.607
  b) 8.27, 8.206, 8.271, 6.49, 6.05, 8.93

Rounding

Rounding to the nearest 10, 100, 1000 B1 B2

Large numbers are often rounded to the nearest ten, hundred or thousand to make them easier to work with.

Rounding to the nearest ten
Look at the **digit** in the units column. If it is **less than 5, round down**. If it is **5 or more, round up**.

Example
276 people went to the theatre to see the opening night of a play. Round this to the nearest ten.

There is a 6 in the units column.
6 > 5, so round up to 280.
276 is 280 to the nearest ten.

Rounding to the nearest hundred
Look at the digit in the tens column. If it is less than 5, round down. If it is 5 or more, round up.

Example
One day in July, 3250 people went to a theme park. Round this to the nearest hundred.

Since there is a 5 in the tens column, you round up to 3300.
3250 is 3300 to the nearest hundred.

Rounding to the nearest thousand
Look at the digits in the hundreds column. The same rules apply as for rounding to the nearest ten or hundred.

Example
17436 people attended a football match. Round this to the nearest thousand.

There is a 4 in the hundreds column, so round down to 17000.
17436 is 17000 to the nearest thousand.

Similar methods can be used to round any number to any power of 10.

Rounded numbers are often used in newspaper reports.

NEWS
20000 revellers at pop concer[t]

Decimal places (d.p.) [B1] [B2]

When rounding numbers to a specified number of **decimal places**, follow these steps:

1. Look at the last number that is wanted (e.g. if rounding 12.367 to 2 decimal places, look at the 6 which is the second decimal place).
2. Look at the number to the right of it (the number that is not needed – in this case, the 7).
3. If it is **5 or more**, then **round up** the last digit (7 is greater than 5, so round up the 6 to a 7).
4. If it is **less than 5**, then the last digit remains the **same**.

In athletics, times are usually rounded to 2 decimal places. The men's 100m world record holder in 2009 was Usain Bolt, of Jamaica, with a time of 9.58 seconds (2 d.p.).

Examples

a) Round 12.49 to 1 decimal place.

12.**49** rounds up to 12.5

b) Round 8.735 to 2 decimal places.

8.73**5** rounds up to 8.74

c) Round 9.624 to 2 decimal places.

9.62**4** rounds down to 9.62

Significant figures (s.f. or sig. fig.) [B1] [B2]

The first significant figure is the first digit that is not zero. The 2nd, 3rd, 4th... significant figures follow on after the first digit. They may or may not be zeros. For example:

6.4027 has 5 s.f.
1st 2nd 3rd 4th 5th

0.0004701 has 4 s.f.
1st 2nd 3rd 4th

To round a number to a given number of significant places, apply the same rule as with decimal places: if the next digit is 5 or more, round up.

For example:

Number	to 3 s.f.	to 2 s.f.	to 1 s.f.
4.207	4.21	4.2	4
4379	4380	4400	4000
0.006 209	0.006 21	0.0062	0.006

After rounding the last digit, you must fill in the end zeros.

For example, 4380 = 4400 to 2 s.f. (not 44).

In 2009, the tallest structure in the world was the Burj Dubai at a height of 828m; that is 800m correct to 1 s.f.

⊘ *Take care when rounding that you do not change the place values.*

Quick test

1. Round the following numbers to 2 decimal places.
   a) 6.429   **b)** 18.607   **c)** 14.271   **d)** 29.638

2. Round the following numbers to 2 significant figures.
   a) 2768   **b)** 271   **c)** 38946   **d)** 0.0273

3. The length of the River Nile is 6650km. What is this length correct to 2 significant figures?

Indices

Number

Indices B2

An index (plural: **indices**) is sometimes known as a power.
For example:
- 6^4 is read as '6 to the power of 4'.
  It means $6 \times 6 \times 6 \times 6$.
- 2^7 is read as '2 to the power of 7'.
  It means $2 \times 2 \times 2 \times 2 \times 2 \times 2 \times 2$.

The base has to be the same when the rules of indices are applied.

$$a^b$$

The base $\longrightarrow$ The index or power

Rules of indices B2

You need to learn the following rules.

Rule 1
When **multiplying**, **add** the powers.
$$4^7 \times 4^3 = 4^{7+3} = 4^{10}$$
Since:
$$(4 \times 4 \times 4 \times 4 \times 4 \times 4 \times 4) \times (4 \times 4 \times 4) =$$
$$4 \times 4 \times 4 \times 4 \times 4 \times 4 \times 4 \times 4 \times 4 \times 4$$

Rule 2
When **dividing**, **subtract** the powers.
$$6^9 \div 6^4 = 6^{9-4} = 6^5$$
Since:
$$\frac{\cancel{6} \times \cancel{6} \times \cancel{6} \times \cancel{6} \times 6 \times 6 \times 6 \times 6 \times 6}{\cancel{6} \times \cancel{6} \times \cancel{6} \times \cancel{6}}$$
$$= 6 \times 6 \times 6 \times 6 \times 6$$

Rule 3
Anything to the **power 1** is just **itself**.
$$15^1 = 15 \qquad 1923^1 = 1923$$

Rule 4
When raising one power to another, multiply the powers.
$$(3^2)^4 = 3^{2 \times 4} = 3^8$$
$$(6^3)^5 = 6^{3 \times 5} = 6^{15}$$

The above rules also apply when the powers are negative.

Here are some examples of the rules in action:
$$6^2 \times 6^{12} = 6^{2+12} = 6^{14}$$
$$5^6 \div 5^4 = 5^{6-4} = 5^2$$
$$8^4 \times 8^3 = 8^{4+3} = 8^7$$
$$4^3 \times 4^{10} = 4^{3+10} = 4^{13}$$
$$7^{10} \div 7^4 = 7^{10-4} = 7^6$$
$$(4^3)^2 = 4^{3 \times 2} = 4^6$$
$$(5^7)^3 = 5^{7 \times 3} = 5^{21}$$

Examples
a) Evaluate $5^1 \times 5^2$

$$5^1 \times 5^2 = 5^3 = 125$$

b) Evaluate $8^6 \div 8^4$

$$8^6 \div 8^4 = 8^2 = 64$$

ⓘ *Evaluate means 'work out'.*

Indices and algebra | B2

The rules that apply with numbers also apply to algebra.

Laws of indices

$a^n \times a^m = a^{n+m}$
$a^n \div a^m = a^{n-m}$
$a^1 = a$
$(a^n)^m = a^{n \times m}$

Examples

a) Simplify $x^4 \times x^7$

$x^4 \times x^7 = x^{11}$

b) Simplify $a^{10} \div a^4$

$a^{10} \div a^4 = a^6$

c) Simplify $\dfrac{x^9}{x^4}$

$\dfrac{x^9}{x^4} = x^5$

d) Simplify $(a^4)^2$

$(a^4)^2 = a^{4 \times 2} = a^8$

e) Simplify $4x^2 \times 3x^5$

$4x^2 \times 3x^5 = 12x^7$

> Note that the numbers are multiplied...

> ...but the powers of the same term are added.

f) Simplify $a^4 \times 3a^5$

$a^4 \times 3a^5 = 3a^9$

g) Simplify $12x^5 \div 2x^2$

$12x^5 \div 2x^2 = 6x^3$

> Note that the numbers are divided...

> ...but the powers of the same term are subtracted.

h) Simplify $15p^9 \div 3p^4$

$15p^9 \div 3p^4 = 5p^5$

i) Simplify $\dfrac{3x^7 \times 4x^9}{6x^4}$

$\dfrac{3x^7 \times 4x^9}{6x^4} = \dfrac{12x^{16}}{6x^4} = 2x^{12}$

> Work this out in two stages.

j) Simplify $x^6 \times 4x^3$

$x^6 \times 4x^3 = 4x^9$

k) Simplify $\dfrac{12a^2b^3}{6a^3b^2}$

$\dfrac{12a^2b^3}{6a^3b^2} = \dfrac{2b}{a}$

> Divide the numbers:
> $12 \div 6 = 2$

> Use the laws of indices to simplify each term.

l) Simplify $\dfrac{4a^4b^3}{2ab}$

$\dfrac{4a^4b^3}{2ab} = 2a^3b^2$

m) Simplify $(2x^3)^2$

$(2x^3)^2 = 2x^3 \times 2x^3$

$= 4x^6$

> Either write out fully or...

or $(2x^3)^2 = 2^2x^{3 \times 2}$

$= 4x^6$

> ...use the laws of indices.

n) Simplify $(3x^2)^3$

$(3x^2)^3 = (3x^2) \times (3x^2) \times (3x^2)$

$= 27x^6$

or $(3x^2)^3 = 3^3x^{2 \times 3}$

$= 27x^6$

> 💡 Learn the laws of indices. Work out the more difficult questions in two stages.

Number

Quick test

1 Simplify the following:
  a) $12^4 \times 12^8$ **b)** $9^2 \times 9^4$ **c)** 4^1 **d)** $18^6 \div 18^2$ **e)** $4^7 \times 4^2$ **f)** 1^{20}

2 Simplify the following:
  a) $x^4 \times x^9$ **b)** $2x^9 \times 3x^7$ **c)** $12x^4 \div 3x^2$ **d)** $\dfrac{25x^9}{5x^2}$ **e)** $\dfrac{5x^6 \times 4x^9}{10x^3}$ **f)** $(4x^5)^2$

Percentages 1

Percentages B1 B2

Percentages are fractions with a denominator of 100. % is the percentage sign.

75% means $\frac{75}{100}$

(cancelling this fraction gives $\frac{3}{4}$ which is equivalent to 75%).

75%

Example

A mixed bag of nuts contains 26% cashew nuts, 42% peanuts and the rest are pistachio nuts. What percentage are pistachio nuts?

26 + 42 = 68% other nuts
Percentage of pistachio nuts = 100% – 68% = 32%

Percentage of a quantity B1 B2 B3

The word 'of' means **multiply**. For example, 40% of £600 becomes $\frac{40}{100} \times 600 = £240$

On the calculator, key in

| 40 | ÷ | 100 | × | 600 | = |

To work this out without a calculator, follow these steps:

❶ Work out 10% first by dividing by 10, i.e. 600 ÷ 10 = £60

❷ Multiply by 4 to get 40%, i.e. 4 × 60 = £240

Examples

a) Find 15% of £750, without using a calculator.

$10\% = \frac{1}{10}$ so 10% of £750 $= \frac{750}{10} = £75$

5% of 750 is half of 75 = £37.50

So 15% = £75 + £37.50 = £112.50

b) Find 17.5% of £640, without using a calculator.

10%	= £640 ÷ 10 = £64
5%	= £32
2.5%	= £16
So 17.5%	= £64 + £32 + £16 = £112

c) A jumper is reduced in a sale by 15%. The original price of the jumper was £42. Work out the sale price, without using a calculator.

15% of £42
10% = £42 ÷ 10 = £4.20
5% = £4.20 ÷ 2 = £2.10
So 15% = £4.20 + £2.10 = £6.30
Sale price of jumper is £42 – £6.30 = £35.70

d) A meal for four costs £92.20. VAT (value added tax), a tax that is added on to the cost of most items, is charged at 17.5%.

i) How much VAT is there to pay on the meal?

17.5% of £92.20 $= \frac{17.5}{100} \times 92.20$

$= £16.14$ (to the nearest penny)

VAT = £16.14

This is just like a 'percentage of a quantity' question.

ii) What is the final price of the meal?

Price of meal = £92.20 + £16.14 = £108.34

An alternative is to use the multiplier method:

An increase of 17.5% is the same as multiplying by $1 + \frac{17.5}{100} = 1.175$

£92.20 × 1.175 = £108.34 (to the nearest penny)

e) A sofa is reduced in a sale by 30%. The original price of the sofa was £825. Work out the sale price of the sofa.

Using the multiplier method:
A decrease of 30% is the same as multiplying by $1 - \frac{30}{100} = 0.7$

£825 × 0.7 = £577.50

One quantity as a percentage of another   B3

To find one quantity as a percentage of another, form a fraction and **multiply by 100%**.

Fraction $\xrightarrow{\times 100\%}$ Percentage

Examples

a) In a carton of milk, 6.2g of the contents are fat. If 2.5g of the fat is saturated, what percentage of the total fat content is this?

On the calculator, key in

| 2.5 | ÷ | 6.2 | × | 100 | = |

$\dfrac{2.5}{6.2} \times 100\% = 40.3\%$ (1 d.p.)

b) Jessica got 64 out of 78 in a science exam. Work out her percentage mark.

On the calculator, key in

| 64 | ÷ | 78 | × | 100 | = |

$\dfrac{64}{78} \times 100\% = 82.1\%$ (1 d.p.)

c) In a class of 29 students, four are left-handed. What percentage of the students are left-handed?

On the calculator, key in

| 4 | ÷ | 29 | × | 100 | = |

$\dfrac{4}{29} \times 100\% = 13.8\%$ (1 d.p.)

d) In a survey of 75 people, only 23 people ate five portions of fruit and vegetables a day. What percentage is this?

On the calculator, key in

| 23 | ÷ | 75 | × | 100 | = |

$\dfrac{23}{75} \times 100\% = 30.7\%$ (1 d.p.)

Michael Mathis/iStockphoto/Thinkstock

Number

Quick test

1 Work out 30% of £700.

2 Sarah got 94 out of 126 in a maths test. What percentage did she get? Give your answer to 1 decimal place. 🖩

3 Reece weighed 6lb when he was born. If his weight has increased by 65%, how much does he now weigh? Give your answer to 1 decimal place. 🖩

4

| Super's football boots | Joe's football boots |
| $\frac{1}{3}$ off | 28% off |

If a pair of football boots usually costs £49.99, which shop sells them cheaper in the sale and what is the sale price? 🖩

Percentages 2

Simple interest `B1` `B3`

Simple interest is the interest that is sometimes paid on money in banks and building societies. The interest is paid each year (**per annum** or **p.a.**) and is the same amount each year.

Example
Jonathan has £2500 in his savings account. Simple interest is paid at 4.4% p.a. How much does he have in his account at the end of the year? (This is a 'percentage of' question.)

Method 1
Find 4.4% of £2500.

$$\frac{4.4}{100} \times £2500 = £110$$

Amount in the account at the end of the year = £2500 + £110 = £2610

Method 2
100% + 4.4% = 104.4%
(increasing by 4.4% is the same as multiplying by 100% + 4.4% = 104.4% = 1.044)

Total savings = 1.044 × £2500 = £2610

Interest paid = £2610 − £2500 = £110

Note: If the money was in the account for four years, the interest at the end of the four years would be 4 × £110 = £440, provided the interest rate stayed the same.

NI and tax `B3`

National Insurance (NI)
National Insurance is usually deducted as a percentage from a wage.

Example
Sue earns £1402.65 a month. National Insurance at 11% is deducted. How much NI must she pay?

11% of £1402.65 = 0.11 × £1402.65 = £154.29

Income tax
A percentage of a wage or salary is removed as **income tax**. **Personal allowances** must first be deducted in order to obtain the **taxable income**.

Example
Harold earns £190 per week. The first £62 is not taxable but the remainder is taxed at 20%. How much income tax does he pay each week?

Taxable income = £190 − £62 = £128
20% tax = 0.2 × £128 = £25.60
Tax per week = £25.60

Rate of inflation
The rate of inflation is the average change in prices across the economy. It is usually measured over a 12-month period, in which case it is called the annual rate of inflation.

Example
A basket of food cost £146 in January this year. What would be the expected cost of this basket of food in January next year, based on an annual rate of inflation of 2%?

Method 1
2% of £146

$$\frac{2}{100} \times 146 = £2.92$$

Cost of basket of food = £146 + £2.92
= £148.92

Method 2
An increase of 2% is the same as multiplying by 100% + 2% = 102% = 1.02
1.02 × £146 = £148.92

Number

Profit and loss **B3**

When you make money on the sale of an item, you make a profit. When you lose money on the sale of an item, you make a loss.

$$\text{Percentage profit (or loss)} = \frac{\text{actual profit (or loss)}}{\text{original price}} \times 100\%$$

Examples

a) A second-hand car salesman buys a car for £5200, then sells it for £6800. What is his percentage profit?

Profit = £6800 – £5200 = £1600

$$\text{Percentage profit} = \frac{\text{actual profit}}{\text{original}} \times 100\%$$

$$= \frac{1600}{5200} \times 100\%$$

$$= 31\% \text{ (2 s.f.)}$$

b) Ahmed sold his iPod for £30. He had bought it for £59. What is his percentage loss?

Loss = £59 – £30
    = £29

$$\text{Percentage loss} = \frac{29}{59} \times 100\%$$

$$= 49\% \text{ (2 s.f.)}$$

c) Susan bought a house for £240 000. She sold it for £265 000. What is her percentage profit?

Profit = £265 000 – £240 000 = £25 000

$$\text{Percentage profit} = \frac{25\,000}{240\,000} \times 100\%$$

$$= 10.4\%$$

Being able to answer percentage questions like the examples shown in this section is important – not only because they appear on the examination paper but because you will come across them in everyday life. Most of the examples are 'percentage of' questions.

There are really only two types of percentage questions:

- 'Percentage of'. Here you are given the percentage so you divide by 100.
- Finding a percentage. Here you need to work out a percentage so you multiply a fraction or a decimal by 100.

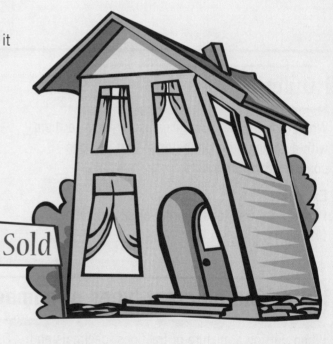

Sold

Quick test

1 Charlotte has £4250 in the bank. If the interest rate is 3.8% p.a., how much interest on the savings will she get at the end of one year?

2 A car costs £6000 cash or can be bought by hire purchase with a 30% deposit followed by 12 monthly instalments of £365. Find...
   a) the deposit
   b) the total amount paid for the car if bought by hire purchase.

3 Fiona has £3200 in savings. If simple interest is paid at 3% p.a., how much will she have in her account after two years?

Fractions, decimals & percentages

Fractions to decimals to percentages B1 B2 B3

Equivalent fractions, decimals and percentages are all different ways of expressing the same number.

The table opposite shows...
- some common fractions and their equivalents, which you need to learn
- how to convert fractions to decimals to percentages.

Fraction	Decimal	Percentage
$\frac{1}{2}$	0.5	50%
$\frac{1}{3}$	$0.3\dot{3}$	$33.\dot{3}$%
$\frac{2}{3}$	$0.6\dot{6}$	$66.\dot{6}$%
$\frac{1}{4}$	0.25	25%
$\frac{3}{4}$ $\xrightarrow{3 \div 4}$	0.75 $\xrightarrow{\times 100\%}$	75%
$\frac{1}{5}$	0.2	20%
$\frac{1}{8}$	0.125	12.5%
$\frac{3}{8}$	0.375	37.5%
$\frac{1}{10}$	0.1	10%
$\frac{1}{100}$	0.01	1%

Ordering fractions B1 B2

When ordering fractions, it is useful to write them with a common denominator so that you can compare the numerators.

Example
Place these fractions in order of size, smallest first. $\frac{1}{4}, \frac{3}{10}, \frac{5}{8}, \frac{7}{20}, \frac{27}{40}$

❶ Since all the fractions can be written with a denominator of 40, we can compare the numerators.
$\frac{10}{40}, \frac{12}{40}, \frac{25}{40}, \frac{14}{40}, \frac{27}{40}$

❷ In size order:
$\frac{10}{40}, \frac{12}{40}, \frac{14}{40}, \frac{25}{40}, \frac{27}{40} = \frac{1}{4}, \frac{3}{10}, \frac{7}{20}, \frac{5}{8}, \frac{27}{40}$

Ordering different types of numbers B1 B2

When putting a mixture of fractions, decimals and percentages in order of size, it is best to change them all to decimals first.

Example
Place the following in order of size, smallest first.
$\frac{3}{5}$, 0.65, 0.273, 27%, 62%, $\frac{4}{9}$

0.6, 0.65, 0.273, 0.27, 0.62, $0.\dot{4}$ — Put into decimals first.

0.27, 0.273, $0.\dot{4}$, 0.6, 0.62, 0.65 — Place in order of size, smallest first.

27%, 0.273, $\frac{4}{9}$, $\frac{3}{5}$, 62%, 0.65 — Rewrite.

💡 *Get a friend to test you on the equivalences between fractions, decimals and percentages as you need to know them.*

Quick test

❶ Change the following fractions into **a)** decimals **b)** percentages. 🖩
   i) $\frac{2}{7}$ **ii)** $\frac{3}{5}$ **iii)** $\frac{8}{9}$

❷ Place the following in order of size, smallest first.
   $\frac{2}{5}$, 0.42, 0.041, $\frac{1}{3}$, 5%, 26%

Using a calculator

Order of operations B1 B2

BIDMAS is a made-up word that helps you to remember the order in which calculations take place.

B I D M A S

Brackets ↑
Indices (or powers) ↑
Division ↑
Multiplication ↑
Addition ↑
Subtraction ↑

BIDMAS simply means that anything in brackets is done first, followed by indices, division and multiplication, then addition and subtraction.

For example:

$(5 + 2) \times 3 = 21$

> Do the calculation in brackets first: $5 + 2 = 7$, then $7 \times 3 = 21$

$5 + 2 \times 3 = 11$

> Here there are no brackets, so the multiplication (2×3) is carried out first, then $5 + 6 = 11$

Important calculator keys B1 B3

🔵 *Make sure you are familiar with the keys on your own calculator.*

Shift or 2nd or Inv allows 2nd functions to be carried out

Allows a fraction to be put into the calculator

(-) or +/– changes positive numbers to negative ones

Bracket keys

Square root

Square

Trigonometric buttons

Memory keys

Works out powers

Cancels only the last key you have pressed

Memory key

Pressing Shift EXP often gives π

Calculating powers B1 B3

$\boxed{y^x}$ or $\boxed{x^y}$ is used for calculating powers, such as 2^7.

Use the power key on your calculator to work out 2^7:
① Write down the calculator keys used.
② Check that you obtain the answer 128.

Write down the keys that are needed for the following calculations. Check that you get the right answers.

$\dfrac{2.9 \times 3.6}{(4.2 + 3.7)} = 1.322$ (3 d.p.)

$9^2 \times 4^5 = 82944$

$\dfrac{3 \times (5.2)^2}{(2.3)^3 \times 5} = 1.33$ (2 d.p.)

🔵 *Make sure you know how to use the power key. It can save lots of time.*

Quick test

① Work out the following on your calculator. 🖩
   a) $\dfrac{27.1 \times 6.4}{9.3 + 2.7}$
   b) $\dfrac{(9.3)^4}{2.7 \times 3.6}$
   c) $\sqrt{\dfrac{25^2}{4\pi}}$
   d) $\dfrac{5}{9}(25 - 10)$

Number

Approximations & checking calculations

Checking calculations   B1   B2   B3

When checking calculations, the process can be reversed. For example:

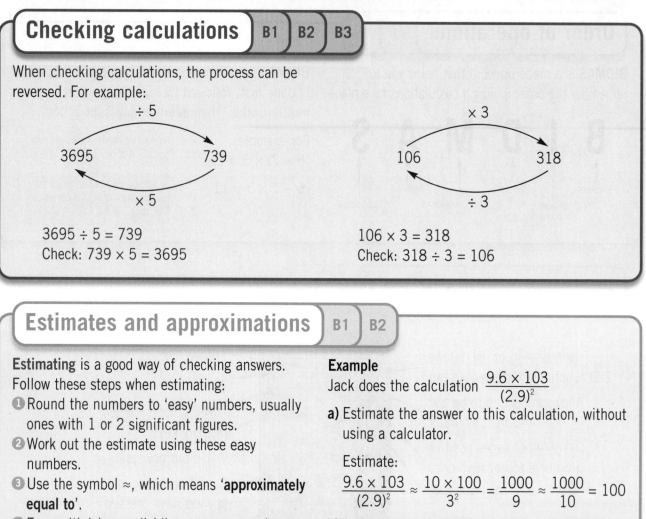

$3695 \div 5 = 739$
Check: $739 \times 5 = 3695$

$106 \times 3 = 318$
Check: $318 \div 3 = 106$

Estimates and approximations   B1   B2

Estimating is a good way of checking answers.
Follow these steps when estimating:

1. Round the numbers to 'easy' numbers, usually ones with 1 or 2 significant figures.
2. Work out the estimate using these easy numbers.
3. Use the symbol ≈, which means '**approximately equal to**'.
4. For multiplying or dividing, never approximate a number to zero. Use 0.1, 0.01, 0.001, etc.

For example:

$8.93 \times 25.09 \approx 10 \times 25 = 250$

$(6.29)^2 \approx 6^2 = 36$

$\dfrac{296 \times 52.1}{9.72 \times 1.14} \approx \dfrac{300 \times 50}{10 \times 1} = \dfrac{15\,000}{10} = 1500$

$0.096 \times 79.2 \approx 0.1 \times 80 = 8$

$\dfrac{602 \times 39}{0.213} \approx \dfrac{600 \times 40}{0.2}$

$= \dfrac{24\,000}{0.2}$

$= \dfrac{240\,000}{2}$ ⟵ Multiply the numerator and denominator by 10.

$= 120\,000$

Example

Jack does the calculation $\dfrac{9.6 \times 103}{(2.9)^2}$

a) Estimate the answer to this calculation, without using a calculator.

Estimate:

$\dfrac{9.6 \times 103}{(2.9)^2} \approx \dfrac{10 \times 100}{3^2} = \dfrac{1000}{9} \approx \dfrac{1000}{10} = 100$

b) Jack's answer is 1175.7. Is this the right order of magnitude (about the right size)?

Jack's answer is not the right order of magnitude. It is 10 times too big.

When adding and subtracting, very small numbers may be approximated to zero.

For example:

$109.6 + 0.0002 \approx 110 + 0 = 110$

$63.87 - 0.01 \approx 64 - 0 = 64$

> 🛈 *Questions that involve approximating are common on the non-calculator paper. For most of these questions, you are expected to round to 1 significant figure. Even if you find the calculation difficult, show your approximations to pick up method marks.*

Number

When solving problems, the answers should be rounded sensibly.

For example:
95.26 × 6.39 = 608.7114 = 608.71 (2 d.p.)
(Round to 2 decimal places because the values in the question are to 2 decimal places.)

Examples

a) Jackie has £9.37. She divides it as equally as she can between 5 people. How much does each person receive?

£9.37 ÷ 5 = £1.874
= £1.87
(Round to 2 d.p. as it is money.)

You will lose marks if you do not write money to 2 d.p. If the answer to a money calculation is £9.7, always write it to 2 d.p., i.e. £9.70

b) Paint is sold in 8-litre tins. Sandra needs 27 litres of paint. How many tins must she buy?

27 ÷ 8 = 3 remainder 3

Sandra needs 4 tins of paint.

Sandra would not have enough paint with 3 tins – she would be 3 litres short. Hence the number of tins of paint must be rounded up.

When rounding remainders, consider the context of the question.

c) The price of a basic calculator is £2.30. Mr Baur wants to buy some basic calculators. He has £70 to spend. Work out the greatest number of basic calculators he can buy.

70 ÷ 2.30 = 30.434... calculators

The greatest number of basic calculators that Mr Baur can buy is 30.

d) Mrs Chan is tiling her bathroom. She needs 43 tiles. Tiles are sold in packs of 8 and cost £15.66 per pack. How much will it cost Mrs Chan to tile her bathroom?

Number of packs of tiles: 43 ÷ 8 = 5.375
She needs 6 packs of tiles.
Total cost = 6 × £15.66 = £93.96

Number

Quick test

1 Estimate the answer to $\dfrac{(29.4)^2 + 106}{2.2 \times 5.1}$

2 Sukhvinder decided to decorate her living room. The total area of the walls was 48m². If one roll of wallpaper covers 5m² of wall, how many rolls of wallpaper did Sukhvinder need?

3 Thomas earned £171.35 for working a 23-hour week. How much was he paid per hour? Check your calculation by estimating.

Ratio

Ratios B1 B2

A ratio is used to compare two or more related quantities:

- '**Compared to**' is replaced with **two dots** (:)
  For example, '16 boys compared to 20 girls' can be written as 16 : 20.
- To simplify ratios, divide both parts of the ratio by their highest common factor.
  For example, 16 : 20 = 4 : 5 *Divide both sides by 4.*

When ratios are simplified as much as they can be, they are in their **simplest form**.

Examples
a) Write the ratio 12 : 24 in the ratio 1 : n

  12 : 24 = 1 : 2 *Divide both sides by 12.*

b) Simplify the ratio 21 : 28

  21 : 28 = 3 : 4 *Divide both sides by 7.*

Look at the flowers shown below. The ratio of red flowers to purple flowers can be written:

$$10 : 4$$
$$= \frac{10}{2} : \frac{4}{2}$$
$$= 5 : 2$$

In other words, for every 5 red flowers there are 2 purple flowers.

Out of every 7 flowers, 5 are red and 2 are purple, so the ratio of 5 : 2 is the same as

$$\frac{5}{7} : \frac{2}{7}$$

Sharing a quantity in a given ratio B1 B2

When sharing a quantity in a given ratio, follow these steps:
1. Add up the total parts.
2. Work out what one part is worth.
3. Work out what the other parts are worth.

Example
£20 000 is shared between Ewan and Leroy in the ratio 1 : 4. How much does each receive?

1 + 4 = 5 parts
5 parts = £20 000, so 1 part = $\frac{£20\,000}{5}$ = £4000

So, Ewan gets 1 × £4000 = £4000 and Leroy gets 4 × £4000 = £16 000

Best buys B1 B2

Compare **unit amounts** to decide which option is the better value for money.

Example
The same brand of coffee is sold in two different-sized jars. Which jar represents the better value for money?

Find the cost per gram for both jars.

100g costs 186p so 186 ÷ 100 = 1.86p per gram.
250g costs 397p so 397 ÷ 250 = 1.588p per gram.

Since the larger jar costs less per gram, it offers the better value for money.

For a non-calculator method, work out the cost of 50g for each jar:

100g = £1.86 so 50g = 186 ÷ 2 = 93p
250g = £3.97 so 50g = 397 ÷ 5 = 79.4p

Hence, the larger jar is better value because it costs less per 50g.

The unitary method is useful when solving ratio problems:

1. Divide to get one part.
2. Multiply for each new part.

Examples

a) A photograph of length 9cm is to have its sides enlarged in the ratio 5 : 3. What is the length of the enlarged photograph?

1. Divide 9cm by 3 to get 1 part.
   $9 \div 3 = 3$
2. Multiply this by 5.
   $5 \times 3 = 15$cm

So the length 9cm becomes 15cm on the enlarged photograph.

9cm

3   3   3

15cm

3   3   3   3   3

b) It took 8 people 6 days to build a wall. At the same rate, how long would it take 3 people?

Time for 8 people = 6 days
Time for 1 person = $8 \times 6 = 48$ days
(It takes 1 person longer to build the wall.)
3 people will take $\frac{1}{3}$ of the time taken by 1 person.

So time for 3 people = $\frac{48}{3} = 16$ days

c) A recipe for 4 people needs 1600g of flour. How much flour is needed to make the recipe for 6 people?

1. Divide 1600g by 4, so 400g for 1 person.
2. Multiply by 6, so $6 \times 400g = 2400g$ of flour is needed for 6 people.

FLOUR

When answering problems of the type shown here, always try to work out what a unit (or one) is worth. You should then be able to work out what any other value is worth.

Number

Quick test

1. Write the following ratios in their simplest form.
   a) 12 : 15   **b)** 6 : 12   **c)** 25 : 10

2. Three sisters share 60 sweets between them in the ratio 2 : 3 : 7. How many sweets does each sister receive?

3. If 15 oranges cost £1.80, how much will 23 of the same oranges cost?

4. A map is being enlarged in the ratio 12 : 7. If a road length was 21cm on the original map, what is the length of the road on the enlarged map?

Practice questions

Use these questions to test your progress. Check your answers on page 94. You may wish to answer these questions on a separate piece of paper so that you can show full working out, which you will be expected to do in the exam.

1 Toothpaste is sold in three different-sized tubes. $\boxed{B1}$

    50ml = £1.24   75ml = £1.96   100ml = £2.42

Which of the tubes of toothpaste is the best value for money? You must show full working out in order to justify your answer. 🖩

2 Arrange these decimals in order of size, smallest to largest. $\boxed{B1}$ $\boxed{B2}$

6.39   5.42   5.04   6.27   6.385   5.032

3 The ingredients for 8 small cakes are...
- 300g self-raising flour
- 250g sugar
- 150g butter
- 2 eggs

Andrew is making 20 small cakes. Write down the amount of...

a) sugar needed   **b)** self-raising flour needed.

4 Mrs Jones inherits £55000. She divides the money between her children in the ratio 3 : 3 : 5. How much does the child with the largest share receive?

5 The price of a television is £999. In a sale, it is reduced by 20%. Work out the sale price of the television. 🖩 $\boxed{B1}$ $\boxed{B3}$

6 Work these out on your calculator, giving your answers to 3 significant figures. 🖩

a) $\dfrac{4.2 \times (3.6 + 5.1)}{2 - 1.9}$ **b)** $\dfrac{3.8 + 4.6}{2.9 \times 4.1}$

7 A school raises £525 at the summer fair. 60% of the money raised is used to repair the tennis courts. How much is used to repair the tennis courts? 🖩

8 From this list of numbers 2, 9, 21, 40, 41, 64, 100... $\boxed{B2}$

a) write down all the numbers that are odd

b) write down all the square numbers

c) write down all the prime numbers

d) write down any numbers that are factors of 80

e) write down any numbers that are multiples of 4.

9 The temperature outside is -6°C. Inside it is 15 degrees higher.

What is the temperature inside? _____

10 A bookstore orders some bookshelves. A bookshelf costs £76. The bookstore needs 589 bookshelves. What is the total cost of the bookshelves?

_____

11 At a school charity concert, £1674 is raised with the sale of 62 tickets. Work out the price of each ticket.

_____

12 Write these numbers in figures.
   a) Fifty-six   **b)** Five hundred and eight   **c)** Seven thousand and two

_____

13 Write the number 6 457 279 in words.

_____

14 Show how you would estimate the answer to this expression without using a calculator. Work out the estimate. $\dfrac{8.7 + 9.02}{0.2 \times 48}$

_____

15 Simplify the following:

   a) $2^3 \times 3^2$ **b)** $a^4 \times a^3$ **c)** $b^6 \div b^2$ **d)** $\dfrac{2a^5 \times 8a^4}{4a^2}$ **e)** $(a^5)^4$

_____

16 A piece of writing paper is 0.01cm thick. A notepad has 150 sheets of paper.   (B3)

How thick is the notepad? _____

17 Hussain scored 58 marks out of 75 in a test. What percentage did he get? 🔢

_____

18 The table shows the cost of a single room at a hotel.

	Cost per person per night excluding VAT	
Day	Friday to Sunday	Monday to Thursday
Low season	£65.00	£95.00
High season	£90.00	£125.00

Frances stays at the hotel for three nights in high season. She arrives on Tuesday. How much does Frances pay for her room, including VAT at 17.5%? 🔢

How well did you do?

| 0–5 | Try again | 6–10 | Getting there | 11–14 | Good work | 15–18 | Excellent! |

Algebra

Algebra

Algebraic conventions B1 B2

Make sure you understand the following conventions of algebra:

- A **term** is a collection of numbers, letters and brackets, all multiplied together.
- Terms are separated by + and – signs. Each term has a + or – attached to the front of it.
- An **expression** is a group of terms, e.g.:

$$3xy - 5r - 2x^2 + 4$$

invisible + sign

xy term

r term

x^2 term

number term

- An algebraic expression must contain at least one letter.
- $3 \times a$ is written without the multiplication sign as $3a$.

$$a + a + a = 3a$$
$$a \times a \times 2 = 2a^2, \text{ not } (2a)^2$$
$$a \times a \times a = a^3, \text{ not } 3a$$
$$a \times b \times 2 = 2ab$$

Collecting like terms B2 B3

Expressions can be simplified by collecting **like terms**. Only collect the terms if their letters and powers are **identical**. For example:

$$4a + 2a = 6a$$

$$3a^2 + 6a^2 - 4a^2 = 5a^2$$

$$4a + 6b - 3a + 2b = a + 8b$$

> Add the a terms together, then the terms with b. Remember a means $1a$.

$$9a + 4b$$

> Cannot be simplified since there are no like terms.

$$3xy + 2yx = 5xy$$

> Remember xy means the same as yx.

The diagram shows a floor plan.

The perimeter of the floor in terms of x is
$$3x + 6 + 2x + 4 + x + 6 + x + 1 + 2x + x + 3$$
$$= 10x + 20$$

Know the words B1 B2

Formula – connects two expressions containing variables, the value of one variable depending on the values of the others. It must have an equals sign, e.g. $v = u + at$. When the values of u, a and t are known, the value of v can be found using the formula.

Equation – connects two expressions, involving definite unknown values. It must have an equals sign, e.g. $x + 2 = 5$. This is only true when $x = 3$.

Function – this is a relationship between two sets of values, such that the value from the first set maps onto a unique value in the second set, e.g. $y = 4x - 1$. For any value of x, the value of y can be calculated.

Multiplying out brackets `B2` `B3`

Multiplying out brackets helps to simplify algebraic expressions. The term outside the brackets multiplies each separate term inside the brackets. For example:

$3(2x + 5) = 6x + 15$ $\quad$ `3 × 2x = 6x, 3 × 5 = 15`

$a(3a - 4) = 3a^2 - 4a$

$b(2a + 3b - c) = 2ab + 3b^2 - bc$

If the term outside the bracket is **negative**, all of the signs of the terms inside the bracket are **changed** when multiplying out.

For example:

$-4(2x + 3) = -8x - 12$ $\quad$ To simplify expressions, first expand the brackets, then collect like terms.

$-2(4 - 3x) = -8 + 6x$

Examples

a) Expand and simplify $2(x - 3) + 3(x + 4)$

$\quad 2(x - 3) + 3(x + 4)$
$= 2x - 6 + 3x + 12$ $\quad$ Multiply out the brackets. Collect like terms.
$= 5x + 6$

b) Expand and simplify $6y - 2(y - 3)$

$\quad 6y - 2(y - 3)$ $\quad$ Take care when multiplying by a negative number.
$= 6y - 2y + 6$
$= 4y + 6$

> If you are asked to 'expand' brackets it just means multiply them out. When you have finished multiplying out the brackets, simplify by collecting like terms in order to pick up the final mark.

Factorisation (putting brackets in) `B2` `B3`

Factorisation is the reverse of **expanding brackets**. An expression is put into brackets by taking out **common factors**. For example:

$$y(x + 4) \xrightarrow{\text{expand}} xy + 4y$$
$$\xleftarrow{\text{factorise}}$$

To factorise $xy + 4y$, follow these steps:
1. Recognise that y is a factor of each term.
2. Take out this common factor.
3. The expression is completed inside the bracket, so that the result is equivalent to $xy + 4y$ when multiplied out.

Examples
Factorise the following expressions.

a) $4a + 8$ $\qquad = 4(a + 2)$

b) $3b + 6$ $\qquad = 3(b + 2)$

c) $3x^2 + 9$ $\qquad = 3(x^2 + 3)$

d) $5x^2 + x$ $\qquad = x(5x + 1)$

e) $4m^2 + 8m$ $\qquad = 4m(m + 2)$

f) $10a^2 - 15a$ $\qquad = 5a(2a - 3)$

g) $12xy - 16x$ $\qquad = 4x(3y - 4)$

h) $12x - 4$ $\qquad = 4(3x - 1)$

i) $x^2 - 6x$ $\qquad = x(x - 6)$

Quick test

1. Simplify these expressions by collecting like terms.
   a) $5a + 2a + 3a$
   b) $6a - 3b + 4b + 2a$
   c) $5x - 3x + 7x - 2y + 6y$
   d) $3xy^2 - 2x^2y + 6x^2y - 8xy^2$

2. Multiply out the brackets and simplify where possible.
   a) $3(x + 2)$
   b) $2(x + y)$
   c) $-3(2x + 4)$
   d) $5(x + 2) + 3(x + 1)$
   e) $2(x - 1) + 5(x + 2)$
   f) $6(2x + 1) - 2(x - 3)$

3. Factorise the following:
   a) $4x^2 + 2$
   b) $2y - 4$
   c) $6x + 10$
   d) $3x^2 + 9x$
   e) $15x - 20x^2$
   f) $x^2 - 5x$

Equations 1

Equations B3

An **equation** involves finding an unknown value that has to be worked out.

Here is an example of an equation:
$3x - 5 = 10$

Solving simple linear equations B3

An equation has two parts separated by an equals sign. When working out the unknown value in an equation, the **balance method** is used; that is, whatever you do to one side of an equation you must do the same to the other side.

Examples

a) Solve these equations.

i) $n - 7 = 10$

$n = 10 + 7$ Add 7 to both sides.

$n = 17$

ii) $n + 6 = 8$

$n = 8 - 6$ Subtract 6 from both sides.

$n = 2$

iii) $3n = 21$

$n = \dfrac{21}{3}$ Divide both sides by 3.

$n = 7$

iv) $\dfrac{n}{4} = 3$

$n = 3 \times 4$ Multiply both sides by 4.

$n = 12$

v) $\dfrac{15}{n} = 5$

$15 = 5n$ Multiply both sides by n.

$\dfrac{15}{5} = n$ Divide both sides by 5.

$n = 3$

b) I think of a number, add 7 and my answer is -5. What is my number?

Let n be the number:

$n + 7 = -5$

$n = -5 - 7$ Subtract 7 from both sides.

$n = -12$

Solving linear equations of the form $ax + b = c$ B3

Remember, use the balance method; whatever is done to one side of the equation must be done to the other.

Examples

a) Solve $2x + 15 = 9$

$2x = 9 - 15$ Subtract 15 from both sides.

$2x = -6$

$x = -6 \div 2$ Divide both sides by 2.

$x = -3$

b) Solve $\dfrac{n}{3} + 2 = 6$

$\dfrac{n}{3} = 6 - 2$ Subtract 2 from both sides.

$\dfrac{n}{3} = 4$

$n = 4 \times 3$ Multiply both sides by 3.

$n = 12$

c) Solve $3x - 1 = 7$

$3x = 7 + 1$

$3x = 8$

$x = \dfrac{8}{3} = 2\tfrac{2}{3}$

d) Solve $\dfrac{n}{4} - 2 = 4$

$\dfrac{n}{4} = 4 + 2$

$\dfrac{n}{4} = 6$

$n = 6 \times 4$

$n = 24$

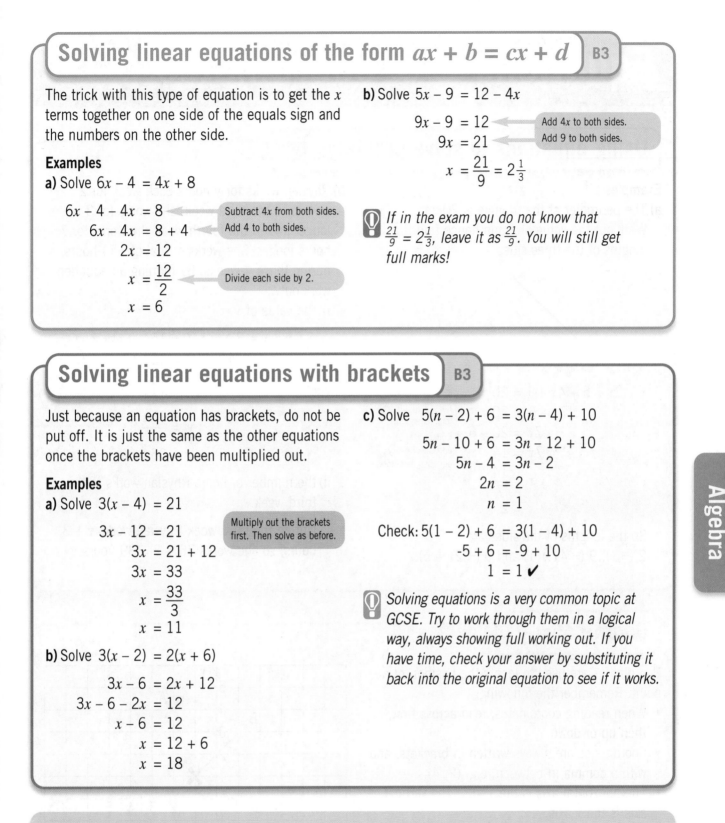

Solving linear equations of the form $ax + b = cx + d$ · B3

The trick with this type of equation is to get the x terms together on one side of the equals sign and the numbers on the other side.

Examples

a) Solve $6x - 4 = 4x + 8$

$$6x - 4 - 4x = 8$$
Subtract $4x$ from both sides.
$$6x - 4x = 8 + 4$$
Add 4 to both sides.
$$2x = 12$$
$$x = \frac{12}{2}$$
Divide each side by 2.
$$x = 6$$

b) Solve $5x - 9 = 12 - 4x$

$$9x - 9 = 12$$
Add $4x$ to both sides.
$$9x = 21$$
Add 9 to both sides.
$$x = \frac{21}{9} = 2\frac{1}{3}$$

💡 If in the exam you do not know that $\frac{21}{9} = 2\frac{1}{3}$, leave it as $\frac{21}{9}$. You will still get full marks!

Solving linear equations with brackets · B3

Just because an equation has brackets, do not be put off. It is just the same as the other equations once the brackets have been multiplied out.

Examples

a) Solve $3(x - 4) = 21$

$$3x - 12 = 21$$
Multiply out the brackets first. Then solve as before.
$$3x = 21 + 12$$
$$3x = 33$$
$$x = \frac{33}{3}$$
$$x = 11$$

b) Solve $3(x - 2) = 2(x + 6)$

$$3x - 6 = 2x + 12$$
$$3x - 6 - 2x = 12$$
$$x - 6 = 12$$
$$x = 12 + 6$$
$$x = 18$$

c) Solve $5(n - 2) + 6 = 3(n - 4) + 10$

$$5n - 10 + 6 = 3n - 12 + 10$$
$$5n - 4 = 3n - 2$$
$$2n = 2$$
$$n = 1$$

Check: $5(1 - 2) + 6 = 3(1 - 4) + 10$
$$-5 + 6 = -9 + 10$$
$$1 = 1 ✔$$

💡 Solving equations is a very common topic at GCSE. Try to work through them in a logical way, always showing full working out. If you have time, check your answer by substituting it back into the original equation to see if it works.

Quick test

1 Solve the following equations.

a) $x + 6 = 10$

b) $2x = 12$

c) $\frac{x}{5} = 4$

d) $x - 4 = 9$

e) $\frac{x}{2} - 3 = 9$

f) $4x + 2 = 20$

g) $5x + 3 = 2x + 9$

h) $6x - 1 = 15 + 2x$

i) $3(x + 2) = x + 4$

j) $2(x - 1) = 6(2x + 2)$

Algebra

Equations 2 & coordinates

Using equations to solve problems · B3

Examples

a) The perimeter of the triangle is 20cm. Work out the value of x and hence find the lengths of the three sides.

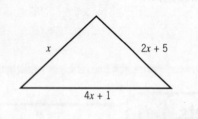

x $2x + 5$

$4x + 1$

$x + 2x + 5 + 4x + 1 = 20$

$7x + 6 = 20$

$7x = 20 - 6$

$7x = 14$

$x = \dfrac{14}{7}$

$x = 2$

> The perimeter is found by adding the lengths together.
> Collect like terms and solve the equation as before.

So the lengths of the sides are
2 (= x), 9 (= $4x + 1$) and 9 (= $2x + 5$).

b) Rhysian works for y hours each week for 2 weeks. In the third week, she works for 3 hours longer and in the fourth week she works for 7 hours longer. She works a total of 154 hours during these 4 weeks. By forming an equation, work out...

i) the value of y

$y + y + y + 3 + y + 7 = 154$ [Write an equation.]

$4y + 10 = 154$

$4y = 154 - 10$

$4y = 144$

$y = \dfrac{144}{4}$

$y = 36$ hours

ii) the number of hours Rhysian works in the third week.

During the third week Rhysian works $y + 3$ hours, so she works $36 + 3 = 39$ hours.

Coordinates · B2

Coordinates are used to locate the position of a point. Remember the following:

- When reading coordinates, read **across first, then up or down**.
- Coordinates are always written in **brackets**, and with a **comma** in between, e.g. (2, 4).
- The horizontal axis is the x-**axis**. The vertical axis is the y-**axis**.

On the grid opposite...

- A has coordinates   (2, 4)
- B has coordinates   (-1, 3)
- C has coordinates   (-2, -3)
- D has coordinates   (3, -1)

On the grid, the midpoint M of the line B (x, y) and D (x_1, y_1) is

$$\left(\left(\frac{x + x_1}{2}\right), \left(\frac{y + y_1}{2}\right)\right)$$

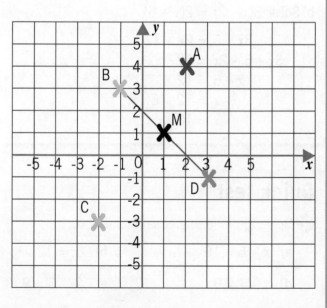

$$\text{Midpoint } M = \left(\frac{-1 + 3}{2}, \frac{3 + -1}{2}\right)$$

$$M = (1, 1)$$

Algebra

Trial and improvement is a method of solving equations by substituting values until a close value is found. This method is particularly useful when solving cubic equations.

Example

The equation $x^3 - 5x = 10$ has a solution between 2 and 3. Find this solution to 2 decimal places.

Draw a table to help.
Substitute different values of x into $x^3 - 5x$.

x	$x^3 - 5x$	Comment
2.5	3.125	Too small
2.8	7.952	Too small
2.9	9.889	Too small
2.95	10.922375	Too big
2.94	10.712184	Too big
2.91	10.092171	Too big

At this stage we know the solution is somewhere between 2.90 and 2.91

Checking the middle value, $x = 2.905$, gives $x^3 - 5x = 9.990\,36...$ which is too small.

| 2.90 | 2.905 | 2.91 |
| (too small) | (too small) | (too big) |

Because $x = 2.905$ is too small, the solution is $x = 2.91$ correct to 2 decimal places.

💡 *Make sure you write down the solution for x, not the answer to $x^3 - 5x$.*

Quick test

1. The equation $y^3 + y = 40$ has a solution between 3 and 4. Find this solution to 1 decimal place by using the method of trial and improvement. 🖩

2. The width of a rectangle is x centimetres.
   The length of the rectangle is $(x + 2)$ centimetres.

   a) Find an expression in terms of x for the perimeter of the rectangle.
      Give your expression in its simplest form.
   b) The perimeter of the rectangle is 40cm.
      Work out the length of the rectangle.

   $4x + 1$

3. What are the coordinates of the points A, B, C, D, E and F?

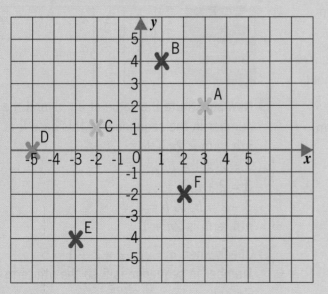

Patterns, sequences & inequalities

Sequences | B2

A **sequence** is a list of numbers. There is usually a relationship between the numbers. Each value in the list is called a **term**.

For example, the odd numbers form a sequence 1, 3, 5, 7, 9, 11, ..., in which the terms have a common difference of 2.

Important number sequences

Even numbers:	2, 4, 6, 8, 10, ...
Square numbers:	1, 4, 9, 16, 25, ...
Cube numbers:	1, 8, 27, 64, 125, ...
Powers of 2:	1, 2, 4, 8, 16, ...
Triangular numbers:	1, 3, 6, 10, 15, ...
The Fibonacci sequence:	1, 1, 2, 3, 5, 8, 13, ...
Powers of 10:	1, 10, 100, 1000, ...

Number patterns | B2

When a number pattern is continued, the numbers relating to a pattern often follow a rule.

Example
Here are the first three patterns in a sequence of patterns made from matchsticks:

a) Draw pattern number 4.

b) Complete the table:

Pattern number	1	2	3	4	5
Number of matchsticks	3	5	7	9	11

c) Explain how you would work out pattern number 7.

Keep adding 2 to the number of matchsticks **or** multiply the pattern number by 2 and add 1.

d) Work out how many matchsticks are in pattern number 13.

$13 \times 2 + 1 = 27$ matches

Finding the nth term of a linear sequence | B2

The nth term gives an expression for the term in the nth position.

The nth term of a sequence is more efficient as it allows any term in a sequence to be found without relying on knowing the previous term.

The nth term of a linear sequence is of the form $an + b$.

Examples
a) Find an expression for the nth term of this sequence: 3, 5, 7, 9, ...

❶ Find the common difference; this is a.
   Difference = 2, so $a = 2$.
   So the nth term = $2n + b$

Term	1	2	3	4 .... n
Number in sequence	3	5	7	9 ....

❷ Now substitute the value of $n = 1$ and the number in the sequence; in this case it is 3.
   nth term = $2n + b$
   $3 = 2 \times 1 + b$
   $3 = 2 + b$
   $3 - 2 = b$, so $b = 1$
   nth term is $2n + 1$

❸ Check when $n = 2$: $2 \times 2 + 1 = 5$
   Number in sequence is 5 so the nth term is $2n + 1$.

b) In a fairground game, a prize is won if the number you pick out of a jar is in the sequence whose *n*th term is $3n + 1$. Josie picks a card with the number 600. Explain whether Josie wins a prize.

$$3n + 1 = 600$$
$$\text{So, } 3n = 600 - 1 = 599$$
$$n = \frac{599}{3}$$

Since 599 is not divisible by 3, Josie does not win a prize.

Inequalities | B3

The inequality symbols are as follows:

> means '**greater than**'
< means '**less than**'
⩾ means '**greater than or equal to**'
⩽ means '**less than or equal to**'

So $x > 3$ and $3 < x$ both say 'x is greater than 3'.

Inequalities are solved in a similar way to equations. Multiplying or dividing by **negative numbers** changes the **direction** of the sign.

For example, if $-x \geqslant 5$ then $x \leqslant -5$.

Examples
Solve the following inequalities.

a) $x + 4 < 10$

$x < 10 - 4$ Subtract 4 from both sides.
$x < 6$

The solution of the inequality $x < 6$ can be represented on a number line:

Use o when the end point is not included.

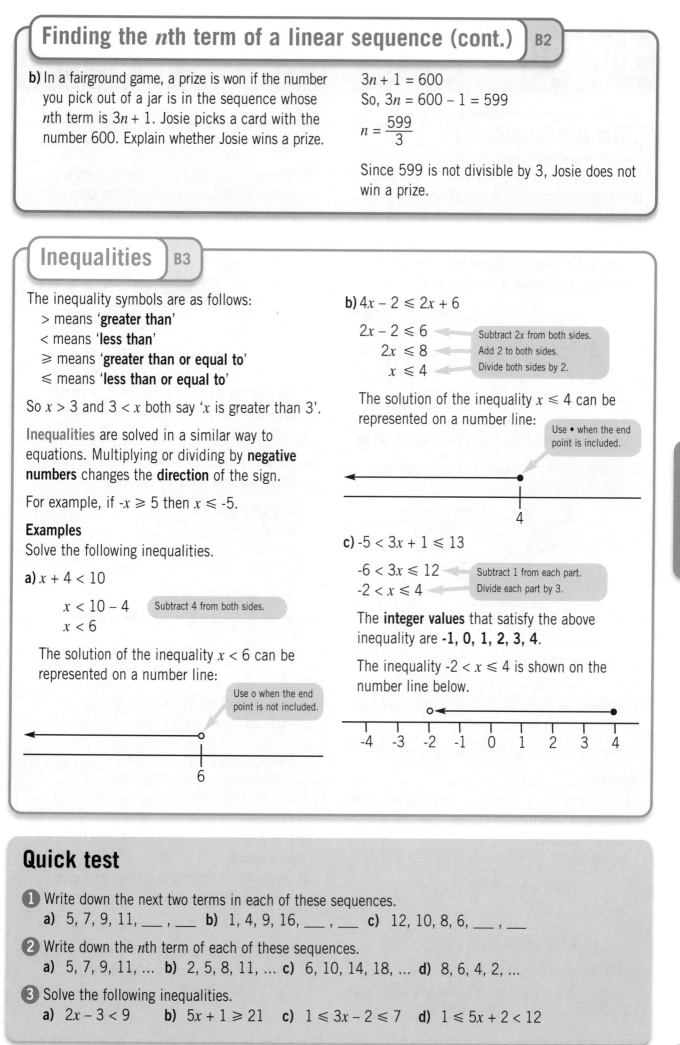

b) $4x - 2 \leqslant 2x + 6$

$2x - 2 \leqslant 6$ Subtract 2x from both sides.
$2x \leqslant 8$ Add 2 to both sides.
$x \leqslant 4$ Divide both sides by 2.

The solution of the inequality $x \leqslant 4$ can be represented on a number line:

Use • when the end point is included.

c) $-5 < 3x + 1 \leqslant 13$

$-6 < 3x \leqslant 12$ Subtract 1 from each part.
$-2 < x \leqslant 4$ Divide each part by 3.

The **integer values** that satisfy the above inequality are **-1, 0, 1, 2, 3, 4**.

The inequality $-2 < x \leqslant 4$ is shown on the number line below.

Quick test

1 Write down the next two terms in each of these sequences.
   a) 5, 7, 9, 11, ___ , ___   **b)** 1, 4, 9, 16, ___ , ___   **c)** 12, 10, 8, 6, ___ , ___

2 Write down the *n*th term of each of these sequences.
   a) 5, 7, 9, 11, ...   **b)** 2, 5, 8, 11, ...   **c)** 6, 10, 14, 18, ...   **d)** 8, 6, 4, 2, ...

3 Solve the following inequalities.
   a) $2x - 3 < 9$ **b)** $5x + 1 \geqslant 21$ **c)** $1 \leqslant 3x - 2 \leqslant 7$ **d)** $1 \leqslant 5x + 2 < 12$

Algebra

Formulae

Writing formulae B3

You need to be able to write a formula when given some information or a diagram.

Examples

a) Frances buys x books at £2.50 each. She pays with a £20 note. If she receives C pounds change, write down a formula for C.

$$C = 20 - 2.50x$$

> Notice that no £ signs are put in the formula.

> This is the amount of money she spent.

If in doubt, check by substituting a value for x. For example, if she bought 2 books $x = 2$, so her change would be $20 - 2.50 \times 2 = £15.00$ ✔

b) Some patterns are made by using grey and white paving slabs.

i) Write a formula for the number of grey paving slabs (g) in a pattern that uses w white ones.

The formula is $g = 2w + 2$

$2w$ represents the 2 layers; $+ 2$ gives the grey slabs on either end of the white ones.

ii) Andy builds a patio using the pattern shown above. He uses 24 white slabs. How many grey slabs will he need to buy?

$$g = 2w + 2$$
$$g = 2 \times 24 + 2$$
$$g = 48 + 2$$
$$g = 50$$

Andy needs to buy 50 grey slabs.

Using formulae B2 B3

A formula describes the relationship between two (or more) variables.

A formula must have an equals sign (=) in it.

Examples

a) Josh hires a van. There is a standing charge of £17 and then it costs £21 per day. How much does it cost for...

i) 6 days?

$$17 + (21 \times 6) = £143$$

ii) y days?

$$17 + (21 \times y) = £(17 + 21y)$$

iii) Write a formula for the total hire cost C.

$$C = 17 + 21y$$

> This is a formula that works out the cost of hiring the van for any number of days.

b) A rule for working out the average carbon dioxide emission from a coach is given by:

$$\frac{\text{Carbon dioxide}}{\text{emission}} = \frac{\text{Distance}}{\text{travelled (km)}} \times 0.17$$

If C stands for the carbon dioxide emission in grams and d stands for the distance travelled in kilometres...

i) write down a formula for the total carbon dioxide emission, C

$$C = d \times 0.17 \text{ or } C = 0.17d$$

ii) work out the carbon dioxide emission for a bus that travels a distance of 28km.

$$C = 28 \times 0.17$$
$$= 4.76 \text{ grams}$$

Formulae, expressions and substituting B2 B3

$p + 3$ is an **expression**.
$y = p + 3$ is a **formula**. The value of y depends on the value of p.

Replacing a letter with a number is called **substitution**. When substituting...
- write out the expression first and then replace the letters with the values given
- work out the value on your calculator. Use bracket keys where necessary and pay attention to the order of operations (BIDMAS).

Examples
a) Using $a = 6$, $b = -3$ and $c = 5$, find the values of these expressions.

i) $5a + 2c$

$5a + 2c = 5 \times 6 + 2 \times 5$
$= 30 + 10$
$= 40$

ii) $\dfrac{3a}{b}$

$\dfrac{3a}{b} = \dfrac{3 \times 6}{-3} = -6$

iii) $2c^2 + 4$

$2c^2 + 4 = 2 \times 5^2 + 4 = 50 + 4 = 54$

iv) $3a^2$

$3a^2 = 3 \times 6^2 = 3 \times 36 = 108$

Remember to show the substitution.

b) The formula $C = \dfrac{5(F - 32)}{9}$ is used to change the temperature from degrees Fahrenheit (F) into degrees centigrade (C). Work out the value of C when $F = -12$.

$C = \dfrac{5(-12 - 32)}{9}$ — Substitute the value of F into the formula.

$C = \dfrac{5 \times (-44)}{9}$ — Work out the brackets first, then multiply by $\frac{5}{9}$

$C = -24.\dot{4}°C$ or $-24\frac{4}{9}°C$

When substituting into an expression or formula you must show each step in your working out. By showing your substitution you will obtain method marks even if you get the final answer wrong.

Algebra

Rearranging formulae B3

The **subject of a formula** is the letter that appears on its own on one side of the formula.

Examples
Make a the subject of these formulae.

a) $v = u + at$

$v - u = at$ — Subtract u from both sides.

$\dfrac{v - u}{t} = a$ — Divide both sides by t.

So $a = \dfrac{v - u}{t}$ — The subject of the formula is usually written first.

b) $b = 3(a - 2)$

$\dfrac{b}{3} = (a - 2)$ — Divide both sides by 3.

$\dfrac{b}{3} + 2 = a$ — Add 2 to both sides.

So $a = \dfrac{b}{3} + 2$

c) $x = ay$

$\dfrac{x}{y} = a$ — Divide both sides by y.

So $a = \dfrac{x}{y}$

Quick test

1. Using $p = 4$, $q = -2$ and $r = 3$, find the value of these expressions.

   a) $3p - 2$ b) $r^2 + 5$ c) $q^2 + 4$ d) $\dfrac{2r^2}{3}$ e) $7q - 4r$

2. Make b the subject of the formula $a = 5b - d$

3. Make m the subject of the formula $y = mx + c$

4. Make R the subject of the formula $V = IR$

Straight-line graphs

Drawing straight-line graphs B2

In order to draw a straight-line graph, follow these easy steps:

1. Choose three values of x and draw up a table.
2. Work out the value of y for each value of x.
3. Plot the coordinates and join up the points with a straight line.
4. Label the graph.

Example
Draw the graph of $y = 3x - 1$.

1. Draw a table with some suitable values of x.
2. Work out the y values by substituting each x value into the equation.

e.g. $x = -2$ ∴ $y = (3 \times -2) - 1$
$= -6 - 1 = -7$

x	-2	0	2
y	-7	-1	5

3. Plot the points and draw the line.

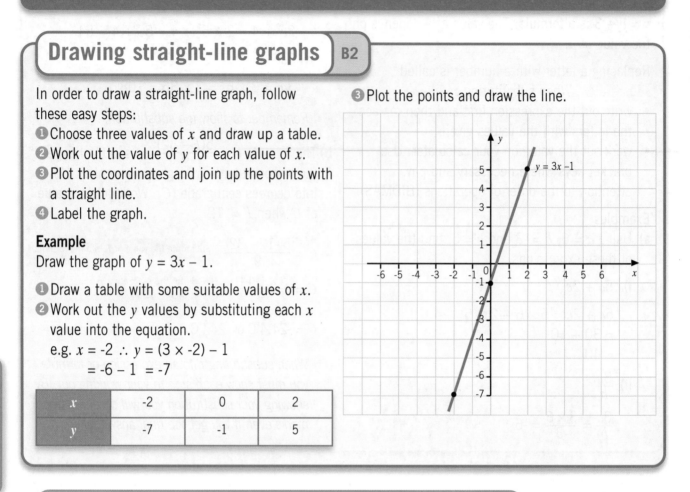

Graphs of $y = a$, $x = b$, $x + y = k$ and $x = y$ B2

$y = a$ is a **horizontal** line with every y coordinate equal to a.

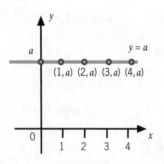

$x = b$ is a **vertical** line with every x coordinate equal to b.

Graphs of $x + y = k$, where k is a number, always give straight-line graphs. Tables of values are not needed when drawing this type of graph.

Graphs of the form $x = y$ are the same as graphs of the form $y = x$.

Examples
a) Draw the graph of $x + y = 3$.

On the x-axis, $y = 0$, so $x = 3$ since $3 + 0 = 3$. On the y-axis $x = 0$, so $y = 3$ since $0 + 3 = 3$. The graph goes straight through the points $(3, 0)$ and $(0, 3)$.

b) Draw the graph of $x = y$.

Where $y = 0$, $x = 0$, where $y = 1$, $x = 1$, etc.

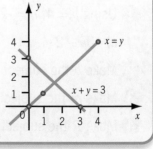

Interpreting $y = mx + c$ B1 B2

The general equation of a straight-line graph is

$$y = mx + c$$

where m is the gradient (steepness) of the line.

Remember these points about straight-line graphs:
- As m **increases**, the line gets **steeper**.
- If m is **positive**, the line slopes **forwards**.
- If m is **negative**, the line slopes **backwards**.
- c is the intercept on the y-axis, that is, where the graph cuts the y-axis.
- **Parallel** lines have the **same gradient**.

It will help if you can sketch a straight-line graph from its equation. If you can do this, you will be able to tell if the graph you have drawn is correct.

As m increases, the line gets steeper.

m is negative, so the graph slopes 'backwards'.

All these lines have a gradient of 2, so they are parallel.

Intercept = (0, -3)

Algebra

Finding the gradient of a line B1 B2

To find the **gradient** of a line, follow these steps:
1. Choose two points on the line.
2. Draw a triangle as shown.
3. Find the change in y (height) and the change in x (base).
4. Gradient $= \dfrac{\text{change in } y}{\text{change in } x}$ or $\dfrac{\text{height}}{\text{base}} = \dfrac{4}{3} = 1\frac{1}{3}$
5. Decide if the gradient is positive or negative (see above).

Do not count the squares as the scales may be different.

(3, 5)

Change in y

(0, 1)

Change in x

Quick test

1. Draw the graph of $y = 6 - 2x$. From your graph, write down the solution of the following equations.
   a) $6 - 2x = 4$ b) $6 - 2x = 3$

2. Write down the gradient and y-axis intercept for each of these straight-line graphs.
   a) $y = 4 + 2x$ b) $y = 3x - 2$ c) $y = 5x - 4$

Quadratic graphs

Graphs of the form $y = ax^2 + b$ · B3

Graphs of the form $y = ax^2 + b$ are known as quadratic graphs because they have a square term in them. They are sometimes called **parabolas**.

Example

Draw the graph of $y = x^2 - 3$.

❶ Work out the y coordinates for several points. Remember that x^2 means x times x.
Replace x in the equation with each coordinate, e.g. when $x = -3$, $y = (-3)^2 - 3 = 9 - 3 = 6$
The table gives coordinates of the points for the graph.

x	-3	-2	-1	0	1	2	3
y	6	1	-2	-3	-2	1	6

❷ Plot and join up the points with a smooth curve, and label the graph.

If you are asked to draw the graph of $y = 2x^2$, remember this means $y = 2 \times (x^2)$.
(Square x first, then multiply by 2.)

$y = x^2 - 3$

Direction of the curve · B3

If the number in front of x^2 is positive, the curve is U-shaped.

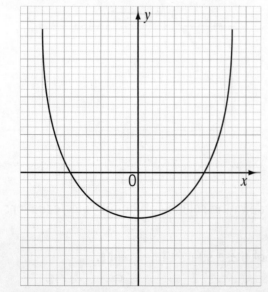

If the number in front of x^2 is negative, the curve is an upside-down U.

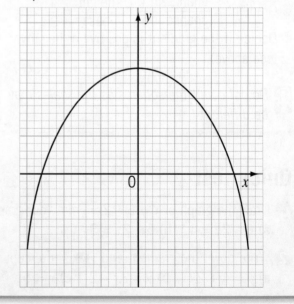

Graphs of the form $y = ax^2 + bx + c$ B3

The following example will help you to understand graphs of the form $y = ax^2 + bx + c$.

Example

Draw the graph of $y = x^2 - x - 6$ using values of x from -2 to 3. Use the graph to find the value of x when $y = -3$.

❶ Make a table of values.

❷ Work out the values of y by substituting the values of x into the equation.

For example, if $x = 1$,
$$y = x^2 - x - 6$$
$$= 1^2 - 1 - 6$$
$$= -6$$

Do not try to input this all into your calculator at once. Do it step by step.

x	-2	-1	0	1	2	3	0.5
y	0	-4	-6	-6	-4	0	-6.25

$x = 0.5$ is worked out to find the minimum value.

❸ Plot the points and join them with a smooth curve.

💡 *Draw the curve with a sharp pencil. Go through all the points and check for any parts that look wrong.*

From the curve below it is clear that...
- the **line of symmetry** is at $x = 0.5$
- the **minimum value** is when $x = 0.5$, $y = -6.25$
- the curve cuts the y-axis at (0, -6), i.e. (0, c).

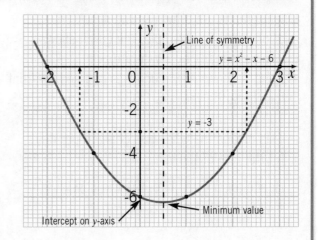

💡 *Show clearly on your graph how you take your readings.*

❹ When $y = -3$, read across from $y = -3$ to the graph then read up to the x-axis: $x = -1.3$ and $x = 2.3$

These are the approximate solutions of the equation $x^2 - x - 6 = -3$.

Algebra

Quick test

❶ **a)** Complete the table of values for the graph $y = x^2 + 3$. 🖩

x	-3	-2	-1	0	1	2	3
y							

b) Draw the graph of $y = x^2 + 3$.

c) From the graph, find the value of x when $y = 8$.

❷ Complete the table of values and draw the graph of $y = 2x^2 - 1$ for values of x from -3 to 3. 🖩

x	-3	-2	-1	0	1	2	3
y							

Interpreting graphs

Graphs in practical situations B1 B2 B3

Linear graphs are often used to show **relationships**. For example, the graph shows the charges made by a van-hire firm:

- Point A shows how much was charged up front for hiring the van, i.e. £50.
- The gradient = 20.
  This means that £20 was charged per day for the hire of the van.

  Hence for 5 days' hire, the van cost
  = £50 + £20 × 5 = £150

$$\text{Gradient} = \frac{120}{6} = 20$$

Cost in £

Number of days

Notice the different scales.

Distance–time graphs B2

Distance–time graphs are often called **travel graphs**. The **speed** of an object can be found by finding the gradient of the line:

$$\text{Speed} = \frac{\text{distance travelled}}{\text{time taken}}$$

Example
The graph represents Mr Rogers' car journey; he sets off at 9am (0900). Work out the speed of each stage of the journey.

a) The car is travelling at 30mph for 1 hour (30 ÷ 1).
b) The car is stationary for 30 minutes.
c) The graph is steeper so the car is travelling faster, at a speed of 60mph for 30 minutes (30 ÷ 0.5).
d) The car is stationary for 1 hour.
e) The return journey is at a speed of 40mph (60 ÷ 1.5).

Notice the importance of using the gradient of a line. It is useful to note that on this distance–time graph example, the scales on the axes are different. Care must be taken when reading the scales: always make sure you understand the scales before you start.

Mr Rogers' car journey

Distance (miles)

Time

Algebra

44

Conversion graphs B1 B2

Conversion graphs are used to convert values of one quantity to another, e.g. litres to pints, kilometres to miles, pounds to dollars, etc.

Example

Suppose £1 is worth $1.50. Draw a conversion graph.

Multiply by 1.5

£1 $1.50

Divide by 1.5

❶ Make a table of values.

£	1	2	3	4	5
$	1.5	3.0	4.5	6.0	7.5

⟩ × 1.5

❷ Plot each of these points on the graph paper.

To change $ to £, read across to the line then down. For example, $4 is £2.65 (approx.).
To change £ to $, read up to the line then across. For example, £4.50 is $6.80 (approx.).

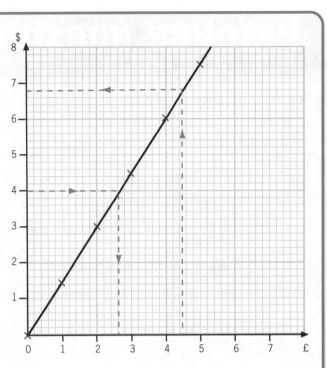

Quick test

❶ The following containers are being filled with a liquid at a rate of 150ml per second.

A   B   C

The graphs below show how the depth of the water changes with time. Match the containers with the graphs.

① ② ③

❷ The travel graph shows the car journeys of two people. From the travel graph find...

a) the speed at which Miss Young is travelling
b) the length of time Mr Price has a break
c) the speed of Mr Price from London to Birmingham
d) the time at which Miss Young and Mr Price pass each other.

Practice questions

Use these questions to test your progress. Check your answers on page 95. You may wish to answer these questions on a separate piece of paper so that you can show full working out, which you will be expected to do in the exam.

Check your answers on page 95.

1 Here are some patterns made out of matchsticks:

1   2   3   4

B2

a) In the space provided, draw pattern 4.

The table shows the number of matchsticks needed for pattern 1 to pattern 3.

b) Complete the table.

c) How many matchsticks are needed for pattern 100? _____

d) Write down a formula connecting the pattern number (p) and the number of matchsticks (m). _____

Pattern number (p)	Number of matchsticks (m)
1	4
2	7
3	10
4	
5	
6	

2 Write down the next two numbers in this sequence: 5, 9, 13, 17, _____, _____

3 Write down the nth term of the linear sequence: 3, 7, 11, 15, 19, ... _____

4 a) Complete this table of values for $y = 3x - 4$.

x	-2	-1	0	1	2	3
$y = 3x - 4$			-4			

b) On graph paper, plot your values for x and y. Join your points with a straight line.

c) Write down the coordinates of the points where your line crosses the x-axis.

B2 B3

5 Multiply out these brackets.

a) $5(n + 2)$ b) $3(n - 2)$ c) $2(n - 5)$ d) $-3(n - 6)$

6 Simplify...

a) $a + a + a + a$ _____   b) $5b - 2b$ _____

c) $3c - 2c + 5c$ _____   d) $6a + 3b - 4b + 2a$ _____

e) $x^5 \times x^2$ _____   f) $3x^2 \times 4x^3$ _____

7 Factorise the following expressions.

a) $5a - 10$ _____   b) $6b + 12$ _____

c) $8y^2 + 12y$ _____

Algebra

8 If $a = b^2 - 6$, then...
   a) calculate the value of a if $b = 3$
   b) calculate the value of a if $b = -4$.

9 The speed of a car can be calculated using the formula $v = u + at$, where v is the speed (m/s) after t seconds, u is the initial speed and a is the acceleration (m/s^2). Find the speed of the car if $u = 10$, $a = 4$ and $t = 12$.

B3

10 Solve the following equations.
   a) $2x + 4 = 10$ **b)** $3x - 1 = 11$ **c)** $5x - 3 = 2x + 12$
   d) $3(x + 1) = 9$ **e)** $2(x + 1) = x + 3$

11 The perimeter of the triangle is 22cm.
   a) Write an equation for the perimeter of the triangle. _____
   b) Use your equation to find the length of the shortest side of the triangle.

$2x + 2$ $5x + 3$

$2x - 1$

12 Water is being poured into these containers at a rate of 250ml per second. The graphs below show how the height of the water changes with time. Match the containers with the graphs.

A   B   C

Graph 1   Graph 2   Graph 3

13 Write down a formula for the total cost T, in pence, of y balloons at 85 pence each and 8 party poppers at z pence each.

14 The equation $x^3 - 2x = 2$ has a solution between 1 and 2. By using a method of trial and improvement, find this solution to 1 decimal place.

15 Solve the inequality $2 \leqslant 5n - 3 \leqslant 12$

How well did you do?

| 0–3 | Try again | 4–7 | Getting there | 8–11 | Good work | 12–15 | Excellent! |

Algebra

47

Shapes

The circle B2

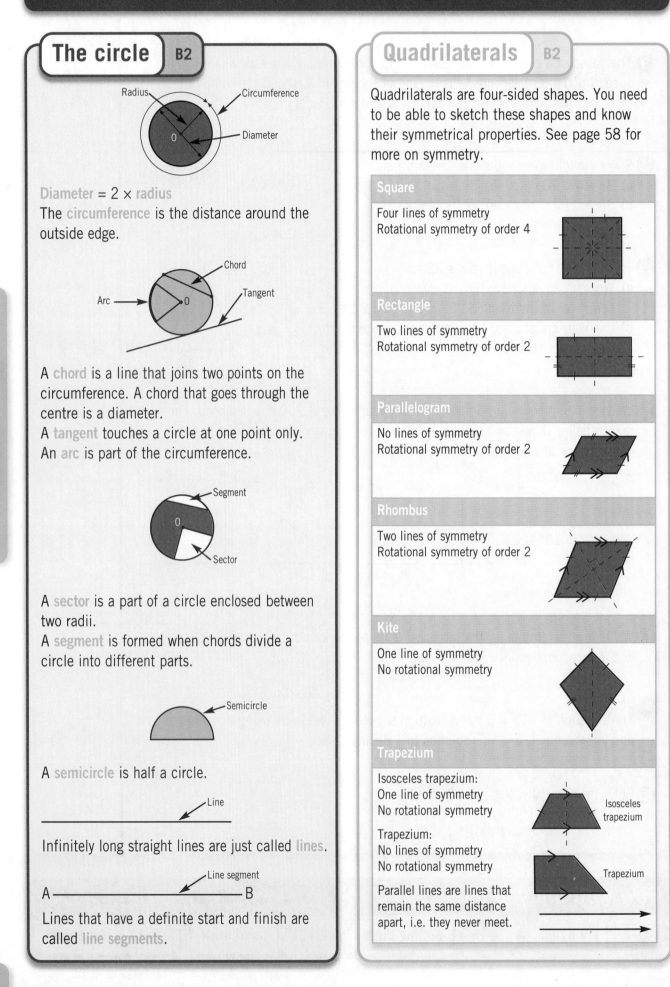

Diameter = 2 × radius
The circumference is the distance around the outside edge.

A chord is a line that joins two points on the circumference. A chord that goes through the centre is a diameter.
A tangent touches a circle at one point only.
An arc is part of the circumference.

A sector is a part of a circle enclosed between two radii.
A segment is formed when chords divide a circle into different parts.

A semicircle is half a circle.

Infinitely long straight lines are just called lines.

A ——————————————— B

Lines that have a definite start and finish are called line segments.

Quadrilaterals B2

Quadrilaterals are four-sided shapes. You need to be able to sketch these shapes and know their symmetrical properties. See page 58 for more on symmetry.

Square
Four lines of symmetry
Rotational symmetry of order 4

Rectangle
Two lines of symmetry
Rotational symmetry of order 2

Parallelogram
No lines of symmetry
Rotational symmetry of order 2

Rhombus
Two lines of symmetry
Rotational symmetry of order 2

Kite
One line of symmetry
No rotational symmetry

Trapezium
Isosceles trapezium:
One line of symmetry
No rotational symmetry

Isosceles trapezium

Trapezium:
No lines of symmetry
No rotational symmetry

Trapezium

Parallel lines are lines that remain the same distance apart, i.e. they never meet.

Polygons `B2` `B3`

Polygons are 2-D shapes with straight sides. Regular polygons are shapes with all sides and angles equal.

💡 *Try to learn all the shapes and their symmetrical properties.*

A regular polygon can be constructed inside a circle.

Number of sides	Name of polygon
3	Triangle
4	Quadrilateral
5	Pentagon
6	Hexagon
7	Heptagon
8	Octagon
10	Decagon

Regular pentagon

It has...
- five equal sides
- a rotational symmetry of order 5
- five lines of symmetry.

Regular hexagon

It has...
- six equal sides
- a rotational symmetry of order 6
- six lines of symmetry.

Regular octagon

It has...
- eight equal sides
- a rotational symmetry of order 8
- eight lines of symmetry.

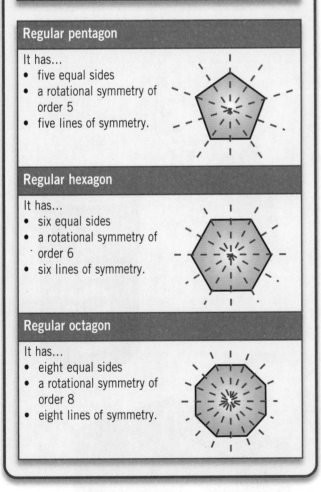

Triangles `B2`

There are several types of triangle.

Right-angled

Has a 90° angle

Equilateral

Three sides equal
Three angles equal
Three lines of symmetry

Isosceles

Two sides equal
Base angles equal
One line of symmetry

Scalene

No sides or angles the same

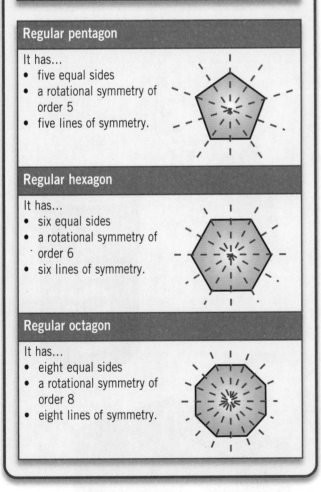

Geometry and measures

Quick test

1 What is the name of a six-sided polygon?

2 From memory, draw all the main types of triangles and quadrilaterals.

Solids

Plans and elevations B3

A **plan** is what is seen if a 3-D (three-dimensional) shape is viewed from above.

An **elevation** is seen if the 3-D shape is viewed from the side or front.

Plan A

Front elevation B

Side elevation C

3-D shapes B2

Cube
A cube has 6 faces, 8 vertices and 12 edges.

Face
Edge
Vertex

Cuboid

Sphere

Cylinder

Cone

Prism
A prism is a solid that can be cut into slices which are all the same shape.

Triangular prism

Square-based pyramid

💡 *Remember to learn the mathematical names of the solids.*

3-D shapes are seen regularly in everyday life.

COLA

BEARINGS R'US
24 in a box

Isometric drawings B2

You can represent 3-D shapes on **isometric paper**. On this paper you can draw lengths in three perpendicular directions on the same scale. The faces do not appear in their true shapes.

A 'T'-shaped prism can be shown clearly on isometric paper (see far right).

Nets of solids B3

The **net** of a 3-D shape is the 2-D (flat) shape that can be folded to make the 3-D shape. For example:

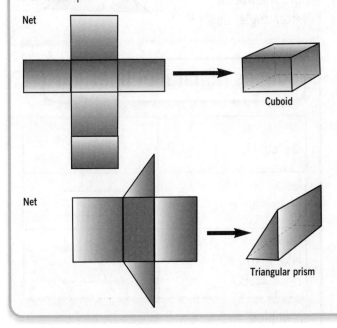

Net

Cuboid

Net

Triangular prism

When asked to draw an accurate net, you must measure carefully.

When making the shape, remember to put tabs on, to stick it together.

In manufacturing, the surface area of the net needs to be kept to a minimum in order to reduce costs.

Quick test

1 Draw an accurate net of this 3-D shape.

5.7cm   4cm
4cm   4cm

2 Draw a sketch of the plan, and elevations from A and B, of this solid.

B

A

Angles

Types of angles | B2

An **acute angle** is between 0° and 90°.

An **obtuse angle** is between 90° and 180°.

A **reflex angle** is between 180° and 360°.

A **right angle** is 90°.

Angle facts | B1 | B2

Angles on a straight line add up to **180°**.
$a + b + c = 180°$

Angles at a point add up to **360°**.
$a + b + c + d = 360°$

Angles in a triangle add up to **180°**.
$a + b + c = 180°$

Angles in a quadrilateral add up to **360°**.
$a + b + c + d = 360°$

Vertically-opposite angles are **equal**.
$a = b, c = d$
$a + d = b + c = 180°$

Reading angles | B2

When asked to find XYZ or $\angle$XYZ or $X\hat{Y}Z$, find the **middle letter angle**, angle Y.

Angles in parallel lines | B2

Alternate angles are **equal**.	
Corresponding angles are **equal**.	
Supplementary angles add up to **180°**: $c + d = 180°$	

Examples

Find the angles labelled by letters.

a)
$a = 180° - 50° - 70° = 60°$
$b = 180° - 60° = 120°$

b)
$a + 80° + 40° + 85° = 360°$
$a = 360° - 205°$
$a = 155°$

c)
$a = 120°$ (angles on a straight line)
$b = 60°$ (vertically opposite to 60°)
$c = 60°$ (corresponding to b or alternate to 60°)
$d = 60°$ (vertically opposite to c)

Measuring angles B1 B2

A protractor is used to measure the size of an angle.

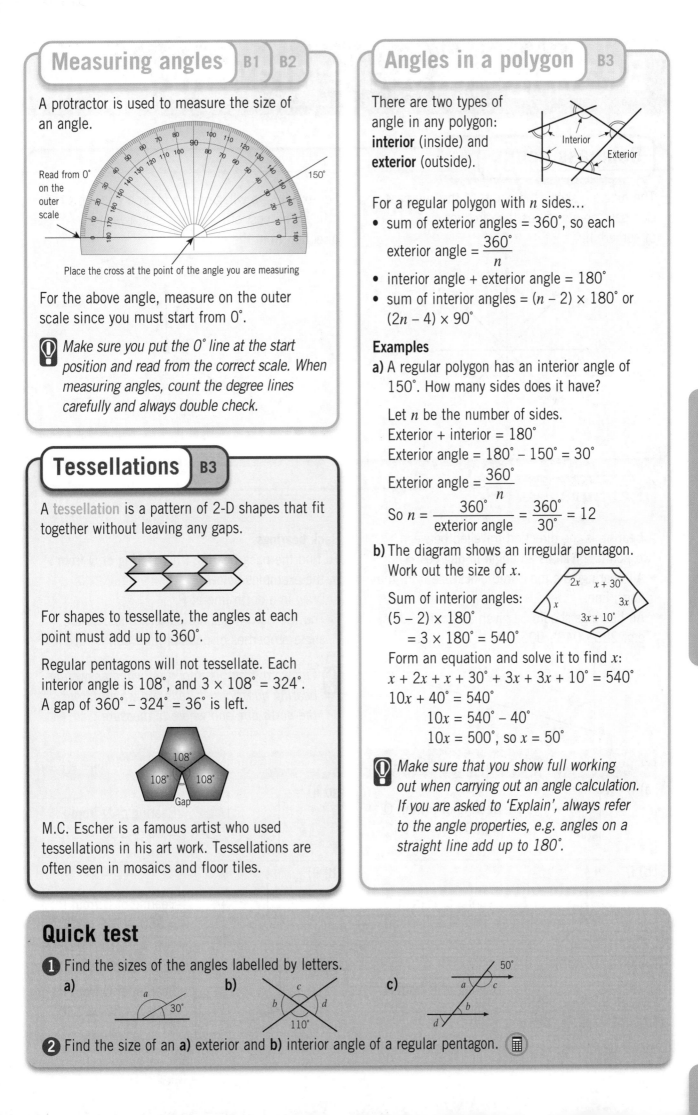

Read from 0° on the outer scale

150°

Place the cross at the point of the angle you are measuring

For the above angle, measure on the outer scale since you must start from 0°.

Make sure you put the 0° line at the start position and read from the correct scale. When measuring angles, count the degree lines carefully and always double check.

Tessellations B3

A **tessellation** is a pattern of 2-D shapes that fit together without leaving any gaps.

For shapes to tessellate, the angles at each point must add up to 360°.

Regular pentagons will not tessellate. Each interior angle is 108°, and 3 × 108° = 324°. A gap of 360° − 324° = 36° is left.

108°
108° 108°
Gap

M.C. Escher is a famous artist who used tessellations in his art work. Tessellations are often seen in mosaics and floor tiles.

Angles in a polygon B3

There are two types of angle in any polygon: **interior** (inside) and **exterior** (outside).

Interior

Exterior

For a regular polygon with n sides...
- sum of exterior angles = 360°, so each exterior angle = $\dfrac{360°}{n}$
- interior angle + exterior angle = 180°
- sum of interior angles = $(n - 2) \times 180°$ or $(2n - 4) \times 90°$

Examples

a) A regular polygon has an interior angle of 150°. How many sides does it have?

Let n be the number of sides.
Exterior + interior = 180°
Exterior angle = 180° − 150° = 30°
Exterior angle = $\dfrac{360°}{n}$
So $n = \dfrac{360°}{\text{exterior angle}} = \dfrac{360°}{30°} = 12$

b) The diagram shows an irregular pentagon. Work out the size of x.

$2x$ $x + 30°$
x $3x$
$3x + 10°$

Sum of interior angles:
$(5 - 2) \times 180°$
$= 3 \times 180° = 540°$
Form an equation and solve it to find x:
$x + 2x + x + 30° + 3x + 3x + 10° = 540°$
$10x + 40° = 540°$
$10x = 540° - 40°$
$10x = 500°$, so $x = 50°$

Make sure that you show full working out when carrying out an angle calculation. If you are asked to 'Explain', always refer to the angle properties, e.g. angles on a straight line add up to 180°.

Geometry and measures

Quick test

1 Find the sizes of the angles labelled by letters.

a)
a
30°

b)
c
b d
110°

c)
50°
a c
b
d

2 Find the size of an **a)** exterior and **b)** interior angle of a regular pentagon.

Bearings & scale drawings

Compass points · B3

The diagram shows the points of the compass. Compass points tell us the direction of something.

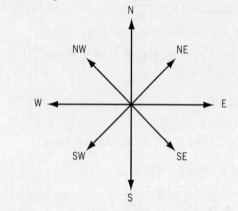

For example, a village has a church and a post office. The post office is in a south-westerly direction from the church.

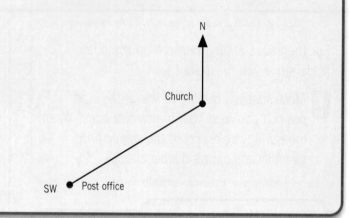

Bearings · B3

A **bearing** is the direction travelled between two points, given as an angle in degrees:
- All bearings are measured clockwise from the north line.
- All bearings should be given as three figures, e.g. 225°, 043°, 006°.

The bearing of A from B

Back bearings

To find the **back bearing** (the bearing of Q from P in the examples below):

1 Draw in a north line at P.

2 The two north lines are parallel lines, so the angle properties of parallel lines can be used.

> The word **'from'** is important when answering bearing questions. It tells you where to put the north line and where to measure.

Bearings (measure from the north line at Q)	Back bearings (measure from the north line at P)

a) i) Bearing of P **from** Q = 060°

b) i) Bearing of P **from** Q = 180° − 30° = 150°

c) i) Bearing of P **from** Q = 360° − 50° = 310°

a) ii) Bearing of Q **from** P = 60° + 180° = 240°

b) ii) Bearing of Q **from** P = 360° − 30° = 330°

c) ii) Bearing of Q **from** P = 180° − 50° = 130°

Scale drawings and bearings B3

Scale drawings are useful for finding lengths and angles. They are often used by architects and surveyors.

Example

A ship sails from a harbour for 15km on a bearing of 040°, then continues due east for 20km. Make a scale drawing of this journey using a scale of 1cm to 5km. How far will the ship have to sail to get back to the harbour by the shortest route? What will the bearing be?

Shortest route = 6.4 × 5km = 32km
Bearing = 70° + 180° = 250°

Shortest route = 6.4 × 5km
(This distance is measured from your diagram using a ruler.)

Note – this diagram is not drawn to scale but is used to show you what your diagram should look like.

Scales and maps B3

Scales are often used on maps. They are usually written as a ratio. You will do map work in geography. Orienteers use maps and compasses to find directions.

💡 *A scale of 1 : 25 000 means that 1cm on the scale drawing represents a real length of 25 000cm.*

Example

The scale on a road map is 1 : 25 000. Bury and Oldham are 60cm apart on the map. Work out the real distance, in km, between Bury and Oldham.

❶ Scale 1 : 25 000, distance on map is 60cm.
∴ Real distance = 60 × 25 000 = 1 500 000cm
❷ Divide by 100 to change cm to m:
1 500 000 ÷ 100 = 15 000m
❸ Divide by 1000 to change m to km:
15 000 ÷ 1000 = 15km

Quick test

❶ What are the bearings of A from B in the following diagrams?

a) 72°

b) 55°

c) 35°

❷ For each of the questions above, work out the bearing of B from A. 🖩

❸ The scale on a road map is 1 : 50 000. If two towns are 14cm apart on the map, work out the real distance between them in kilometres. 🖩

Constructions

Constructing a triangle — B3

To construct this triangle using a compass and a ruler, you would follow these steps:
1. Draw the longest side.
2. With the compass point at A, draw an arc of radius 4cm.
3. With the compass point at B, draw an arc of radius 5cm.
4. Join A and B to the point where the two arcs meet at C.

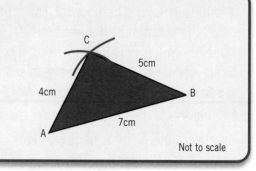

Not to scale

The perpendicular bisector of a line segment — B3

To construct the **perpendicular bisector** of the **line segment** XY, you would follow these steps:
1. Draw two arcs with a compass, using X as the centre. The compass must be set at a radius greater than half the distance of XY.
2. Draw two more arcs with Y as the centre. (Keep the compass the same distance apart as before.)
3. Join the two points where the arcs cross.
4. AB is the **perpendicular bisector** of XY.
5. N is the **midpoint** of XY.

The perpendicular from a point to a line — B3

To construct the perpendicular from point P to the line AB, you would follow these steps:
1. From P draw arcs to cut the line at A and B.
2. From A and B draw arcs with the same radius to intersect at a point C below the line.
3. Join P to C; this line is perpendicular to AB.

Constructing an angle of 60° — B3

To construct an angle of 60° at point P on a line segment XY, you would follow these steps:
1. Put the compass point on P and draw an arc.
2. Label, with an N, the point where the arc intersects the line segment XY.
3. Keeping the radius the same, from point N draw an arc to intersect the first arc at point R.
4. Join PR. Angle RPN is 60°.

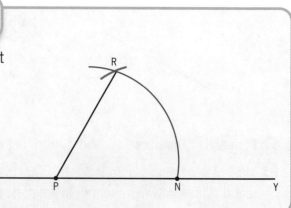

The perpendicular from a point on a straight line　B3

To construct the perpendicular at the point N on
a straight line, you would follow these steps:
1. With the compass set to a radius of several
   centimetres, and centred on N, draw arcs to
   cut the line at A and B.
2. Construct the **perpendicular bisector** of the line
   segment AB as on page 56.

Bisecting an angle　B3

To bisect an angle, follow these steps:
1. Draw two lines, XY and YZ, to meet at an angle.
2. Using a compass, place the point at Y and
   draw the two arcs on XY and YZ.
3. Place the compass point at the two arcs on XY
   and YZ, and draw arcs to cross at N.
4. Join Y and N. YN is the **bisector** of angle XYZ.

Construction of an inscribed regular polygon　B3

Example
Construct a regular hexagon inside a circle of radius 2cm.

Draw a circle of radius 2cm
and mark a point P on its
circumference.

Keeping the compass set at
2cm, draw an arc, centre P,
which cuts the circle at Q.
Q is the centre of the next arc.

Repeat the process until six
points are marked on the
circumference. Join the
points to make a hexagon.

Quick test

1. Bisect this angle.
2. Draw the perpendicular
   bisector of a 10cm line.

Diagram drawn to scale

Symmetry

Reflective symmetry B2

Reflective symmetry is when both sides of a symmetrical shape are the same when the mirror line is drawn across it. The mirror line is known as the line or axis of symmetry.

One line of symmetry

One line of symmetry

Three lines of symmetry

No lines of symmetry

The diagram shows how the line of symmetry acts as a mirror line. The reflected shape is exactly the same as the object.

Mirror line

Object | Reflected shape

Line of symmetry

ⓘ *You may be asked to complete an object with a specific number of lines of symmetry. Draw the reflected shape carefully using a ruler.*

Rotational symmetry B2

A 2-D shape has rotational symmetry if, when turned about the centre, it looks exactly the same.

The **order of rotational symmetry** is the number of times the shape looks the same within one complete turn (360°). For the letter M, the shape has 1 such position. It is said to have rotational symmetry of order 1, or no rotational symmetry. The same is true for the letter T.

Order 1 or no rotational symmetry

Order 1

Order 3

Order 4

Quick test

❶ On the grid opposite, the dashed lines are the lines of symmetry. Complete the shape so that it is symmetrical.

❷ Draw the lines of symmetry on the shapes below.

a)

b)

❸ What is the order of rotational symmetry of a rectangle?

58

Loci

Common loci B3

The locus of a point is the set of all the possible positions which that point can occupy, subject to some given condition or rule. The plural of locus is loci.

Remember these points:

- The locus of the points that are a constant distance (**equidistant**) from a fixed point, P, is a circle.

- The locus of the points that are equidistant from two points, X and Y, is the perpendicular bisector of the line XY.

- The locus of the points that are equidistant from two non-parallel lines is the line that bisects the angle between the two lines.

- The locus of the points that are a constant distance from a line is a pair of parallel lines above and below the line.

- The locus of the points that are a constant distance from a line segment, XY, is a pair of parallel lines above and below XY, and semicircles at either end.

Example

The diagram shows a gas depot and train station in relation to a built-up area. A new hospital (H) is being built so that it is equidistant from the train station and the gas depot. The hospital cannot be within 80m of the gas depot in case of a leak. Using a scale of 1cm to 20m, show the first available position where the hospital can be built.

❶ Construct the perpendicular bisector of the line between the train station and the gas depot.

❷ With the compass point on the gas depot, draw a circle of radius 4cm since the hospital cannot be built within 80m of the depot.

❸ The first available position of the hospital (H) is shown.

This diagram is not drawn to scale but shows you what your diagram should look like.

💡 *When answering loci questions, use the construction techniques previously shown: this will ensure your work is accurate.*

Quick test

❶ A gold coin is buried in the rectangular field. It is 4m from T and equidistant from RU and RS. Copy the diagram to a scale of 1cm : 1m and mark with an X the position of the gold coin.

Transformations 1

Transformations B3

A transformation changes the position or size of a shape. There are four types of transformations: translations, reflections, rotations and enlargements.

Transformations are often used in the creation of repeating wallpaper patterns.

Translations B3

A **translation** moves a figure from one place to another. The size and shape of the figure are not changed. **Vectors** are used to describe the distance and direction of a translation.

A vector is written $\binom{a}{b}$, where **a** represents the **horizontal** movement, and **b** represents the **vertical** movement. The original shape is the object. The shape in the new position is called the **image**.

Example
a) Translate ABC by the vector $\binom{2}{1}$. Call the image P.

> This means 2 to the right and 1 upwards.

b) Translate ABC by the vector $\binom{-3}{-2}$. Call the image Q.

> This means 3 to the left and 2 down.

P and Q are **congruent** – two shapes are congruent if they have exactly the same size and shape.

Reflections B3

A **reflection** creates an image of an object on the other side of the **mirror line**. The size and shape of the figure are not changed.

Example
Reflect triangle ABC in...
a) the x-axis, and call the image D
b) the line $y = -x$, and call the image E
c) the line $x = 5$, and call the image F.

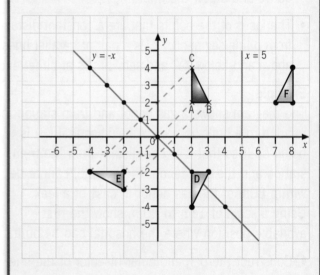

Triangles D, E and F are congruent to triangle ABC.

When describing reflections, make sure you write down the equation of the mirror line.

> *Count the squares to find the distance from the object to the mirror line.*

A **rotation** turns a figure through an angle about some fixed point. This fixed point is called the **centre of rotation**. The size and shape of the figure are not changed.

Example

Rotate triangle ABC...

a) 90° clockwise about (0, 0), and call it R

b) 180° about (0, 0), and call it S

c) 90° anticlockwise about (-1, 1), and call it T.

Triangles R, S and T are all congruent to triangle ABC.

💡 When describing a rotation, give...
- the centre of rotation
- the direction of the turn (clockwise or anticlockwise)
- the angle of the turn.

If you do not give all three pieces of information, you will lose marks for not describing the rotation fully.

Quick test

1. On the diagram opposite...
   a) translate triangle ABC by the vector $\binom{-3}{1}$, and call it P
   b) reflect ABC in the line $y = x$, and call it Q
   c) reflect ABC in the line $y = -1$, and call it R
   d) rotate ABC 180° about (0, 0), and call it S.

2. What does the vector $\binom{-2}{3}$ mean?

3. A point R (3, -6) moves to the point T (-2, 5). What is the vector translation that moves point R to point T?

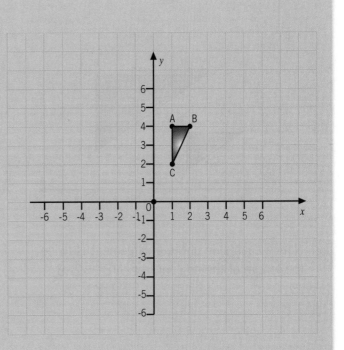

Transformations 2

Enlargements B3

An **enlargement** changes the size but not the shape of an object.

The centre of enlargement is the point from which the enlargement takes place.

The scale factor indicates how many times the lengths of the original figure have changed in size.

Remember the following:

- If the scale factor is **greater than 1**, the shape becomes **bigger**.
- When a shape is enlarged, the perimeter increases by the same scale factor.
- When one shape is an enlargement of another, they are **similar**, i.e. they are the same shape with the same angles, but they are different sizes.

Examples

a) Enlarge triangle ABC by a scale factor of 2, centre = (0, 0). Call it A'B'C'.

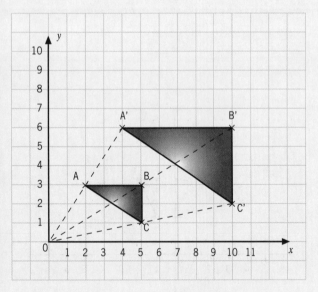

Notice each side of the enlargement is twice the length of the original, e.g. A'B' = 2AB

b) Describe fully the transformation that maps ABCDEF onto A'B'C'D'E'F'.

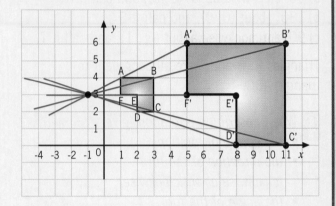

- To find the centre of enlargement, join A to A', and continue the line. Join B to B', and continue the line. Do the same for the others.
- Where all the lines meet is the centre of enlargement: (-1, 3).
- The transformation is an enlargement with scale factor 3 and centre of enlargement at (-1, 3).

Notice that A'B'C'D'E'F' is three times the size of ABCDEF.

When asked to describe an enlargement, you must include the scale factor and the position of the centre of enlargement.

Geometry and measures

Combined transformations are a series of two or more transformations.

Example

a) Reflect triangle ABC in the x-axis and call the image $A_1B_1C_1$.

b) Reflect triangle $A_1B_1C_1$ in the y-axis and call the image $A_2B_2C_2$.

+

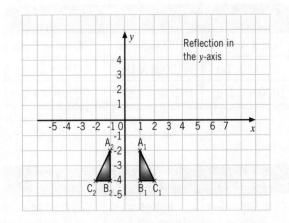

The single transformation that maps ABC directly onto $A_2B_2C_2$ is a rotation of 180° about centre (0, 0).

=

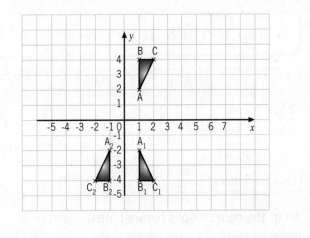

Geometry and measures

Quick test

1 Draw an enlargement of shape P with a scale factor of 2. Call it P1.

2 a) Rotate the shaded shape through a 90° clockwise rotation about (0, 0). Call this shape B.

b) Reflect shape B in the x-axis. Call this shape C.

1

2

Measures & measurement 1

Metric and imperial units `B1` `B2`

Metric units

Length	Weight	Capacity
10mm = 1cm	1000mg = 1g	1000ml = 1 litre
100cm = 1m	1000g = 1kg	100cl = 1 litre
1000m = 1km	1000kg = 1 tonne	1000cm³ = 1 litre

Imperial units

Length	Weight	Capacity
1 foot = 12 inches	1 stone = 14 pounds (lb)	20 fluid oz = 1 pint
1 yard = 3 feet	1 pound = 16 ounces (oz)	8 pints = 1 gallon

Here are some metric conversions:

500cm = 5m   (÷ 100)
25cm = 250mm   (× 10)
3500g = 3.5kg   (÷ 1000)

Example
Change 166 pints into gallons.

8 pints = 1 gallon, 1 pint = $\frac{1}{8}$ gallon
166 ÷ 8 = 20.75 gallons

Converting units
Remember these points:
- If changing from **small** units **to large** units (for example, grams to kilograms), **divide**.
- If changing from **large** units **to small** units (for example, kilometres to metres), **multiply**.

Comparisons between metric and imperial units `B2`

Length	Weight	Capacity
2.5cm ≈ 1 inch	25g ≈ 1 ounce	1 litre ≈ $1\frac{3}{4}$ pints *
30cm ≈ 1 foot *		
1m ≈ 39 inches	1kg ≈ 2.2 pounds *	4.5 litres ≈ 1 gallon *
8km ≈ 5 miles *		

All of the comparisons between metric and imperial units are only approximate.

Example
Change 25km into miles.

8km ≈ 5 miles
1km ≈ $\frac{5}{8}$ mile = 0.625 miles
25km ≈ 25 × 0.625
     = 15.625 miles

*There is a lot of learning to do in this section. Try to learn all the metric and imperial conversions marked *.*

Reading scales `B1` `B2`

Decimals are usually used when reading scales. Measuring jugs, rulers and weighing scales are all examples of scales that use decimals. For example:

There are ten spaces between 8 and 9.
Each space represents 0.1

There are five spaces between 6 and 7.
Each space represents 0.2

There are eight spaces between 12 and 14.
Each space represents 0.25

Estimating measures B1 B2

Estimates using metric and imperial units need to be made all the time.

Estimating lengths

Length and distance can be measured in the following units:
- **Metric:** kilometres (km), metres (m), centimetres (cm) and millimetres (mm).
- **Imperial:** inches, feet, yards and miles.

Some common estimates include:
- A door is about 2 metres high or about $6\frac{1}{2}$ feet.
- A 30cm ruler is about 1 foot long.

Estimating capacities

Capacity is a measure of how much a container can hold. It can be measured in the following units:
- **Metric:** millilitres (ml), centilitres (cl) and litres (l).
- **Imperial:** pints and gallons.

Some common estimates include:
- A 1 pint milk carton holds about 570ml.
- A petrol can holds 1 gallon or 4.5 litres.
- A can of pop holds about 300ml or $\frac{1}{2}$ pint.

Estimating weights (masses)

Weight can be measured in the following units:
- **Metric:** milligrams (mg), grams (g), kilograms (kg) and tonnes (t).
- **Imperial:** ounces (oz), pounds (lb), stones (st) and tons.

Some common estimates include:
- A 1kg bag of sugar weighs about 2.2lb.
- A 250g packet of butter weighs about $\frac{1}{2}$lb.

Door 2m

0   30cm
Ruler 1ft

Milk
1 pint

Petrol can
1 gallon

Pop
$\frac{1}{2}$ pint

Sugar
1kg

Butter
250g

Quick test

1. Change 3500g into kilograms.

2. Change 3kg into pounds.

3. Change 8 litres into pints.

4. What do the pointers on the scales represent?

5. What would be the approximate weight of a newborn baby?
   A 50g   **B** 5g   **C** 3kg   **D** 30kg

Measures & measurement 2

The calendar and time facts B1 B2

A year has 12 months. There are 365 days in a year. In a leap year, there are 366 days because February has 29 days in a leap year.

Here are some other important time facts. There are...
- 60 seconds in 1 minute
- 60 minutes in 1 hour
- 24 hours in 1 day
- 7 days in 1 week
- 52 weeks in 1 year.

Timetables B1 B2

Timetables often use the 24-hour clock.

Timetables should be read carefully. For example, this timetable shows the train times from London to Manchester.

There will be a train from London every 60 minutes (or 1 hour), i.e. 0750, 0850, etc.

London Euston	0602	0650		1100	1300
Watford Junction	0632	0720	Every 60 minutes until	1130	1330
Stoke-on-Trent	0750	0838		–	1445
Manchester Piccadilly	0838	0926		1315	1540

The 0750 train from Stoke-on-Trent

The 0650 train from London arrives in Manchester at 0926.

The 1100 train from London does not stop at Stoke-on-Trent.

The 0632 train from Watford Junction takes 2 hours 6 minutes to travel to Manchester.

If a timetable is written using the 24-hour clock, make sure your answers are in 24-hour clock time.

Reading a timetable is a very important technique to learn. You will be expected to be able to read and interpret a selection of different timetables and charts.

Compound measures — B2

Speed can be measured in kilometres per hour (km/h), miles per hour (mph) and metres per second (m/s). These are all **compound measures** because they involve a combination of basic measures.

$$\text{Average speed} = \frac{\text{total distance travelled}}{\text{total time taken}}$$
$$s = \frac{d}{t}$$

From the speed formula, two other useful formulae can be found:

$$\text{Time} = \frac{\text{distance}}{\text{speed}}$$
$$t = \frac{d}{s}$$

$$\text{Distance} = \text{speed} \times \text{time}$$
$$d = st$$

💡 *Just remember the letters: it's easier. Use the formula triangle to help you.*

$$\frac{d}{s \times t}$$

Always check the units before starting a question. Change them if necessary.

Examples

a) A car travels 70 miles in 2 hours. Find the speed in miles per hour.

$$s = \frac{d}{t} = \frac{70}{2} = 35\text{mph}$$

b) A car travels a distance of 240 miles at an average speed of 60mph. How long does the journey take?

$$t = \frac{d}{s} \text{ so } t = \frac{240}{60} = 4 \text{ hours}$$

Accuracy of measurement — B1 B2

There are two types of measurements – discrete measurements and continuous measurements:
- **Discrete measurements** are quantities that can be counted; for example, the number of baked bean tins on a shelf.
- **Continuous measurements** are measurements that have been taken with a measuring instrument; for example, the height of a person. Continuous measurements are **not always exact**.

For example, Nigel weighs 72kg to the nearest kilogram. His actual weight could be anywhere between 71.5kg and 72.5kg.

These two values are the **limits** of Nigel's weight.

Example
The length of a seedling is measured as 3.7cm to the nearest tenth of a centimetre. What are the upper and lower limits of the length?

Lower limit = 3.65cm and upper limit = 3.75cm.

Quick test

1. What are the upper and lower limits for a time of 9.2 seconds, rounded to the nearest tenth of a second?

2. Write down the upper and lower limits for a weight of 58kg, rounded to the nearest kilogram.

3. Amy walks 6 miles in 2 hours. Find her average speed.

4. Find the time taken for a car to travel 245 miles at an average speed of 70mph.

Pythagoras' theorem

The theorem   B3

Pythagoras' theorem states: in any right-angled triangle, the square on the hypotenuse is equal to the sum of the squares on the other two sides.

The hypotenuse is the longest side of a right-angled triangle. It is always opposite the right angle.

Using the letters in the diagram, the theorem is written as $c^2 = a^2 + b^2$

This can be rearranged to give:
$a^2 = c^2 - b^2$ or $b^2 = c^2 - a^2$
These forms are useful when calculating the length of one of the shorter sides.

Finding the length of the hypotenuse   B3

Remember: Pythagoras' theorem can only be used for right-angled triangles.

To find the length of the hypotenuse (longest side), follow these simple steps:

1. Square the two lengths of the two shorter sides that you are given.
2. To find the hypotenuse, **add** these two squared numbers.
3. After adding the two squared lengths, take the **square root** ($\sqrt{}$) of the sum.

Example
Find the length of AB, giving your answer to 1 decimal place.

Using Pythagoras' theorem:
$(AB)^2 = (AC)^2 + (BC)^2$
$= 12^2 + 14.5^2$
$= 354.25$
$AB = \sqrt{354.25}$ Take the square root to find AB.
$= 18.8\text{m}$ Round to 1 d.p.

Finding the length of a shorter side   B3

To find the length of a shorter side, follow these steps:

1. Square the two lengths of the two sides you are given.
2. To find the shorter length, subtract the smaller value from the larger value.
3. Take the square root ($\sqrt{}$) of your answer.

💡 *Pythagoras' theorem allows us to calculate the length of one of the sides of a right-angled triangle when the other two sides are known. If you are not told to what degree of accuracy to round your answer, be guided by significant figures given in the question.*

Example
Find the length of FG, giving your answer to 1 decimal place.

Using Pythagoras' theorem:
$(EF)^2 = (EG)^2 + (FG)^2$
$(FG)^2 = (EF)^2 - (EG)^2$
$= 9^2 - 8^2$
$= 81 - 64$
$= 17$
$FG = \sqrt{17}$
$= 4.1\text{cm}$

By drawing in a triangle between the two points A (1, 2) and B (7, 6) we can find the length of AB by using Pythagoras' theorem.

Horizontal distance = 6   [7 – 1]

Vertical distance = 4   [6 – 2]

$$\text{Length of (AB)}^2 = 6^2 + 4^2$$
$$= 36 + 16$$
$$= 52$$
$$\text{AB} = \sqrt{52}$$

Length of AB = 7.21 (2 d.p.)

Solving problems | B3

Examples

a) Calculate the height of this isosceles triangle.

❶ Split the triangle down the middle to make it right-angled.

❷ Using Pythagoras' theorem:
$$5^2 = h^2 + 1.75^2$$
$$h^2 = 5^2 - 1.75^2$$
$$h^2 = 21.9375$$
$$h = \sqrt{21.9375} = 4.68\text{cm (2 d.p.)}$$

b) A ladder of length 13m rests against a wall. The height that the ladder reaches up the wall is 12m. How far away from the wall is the foot of the ladder?

$$13^2 = x^2 + 12^2$$
$$x^2 = 13^2 - 12^2$$
$$x^2 = 169 - 144$$
$$x^2 = 25$$
$$x = \sqrt{25} = 5\text{m}$$

The foot of the ladder is 5m away from the wall.

Quick test

❶ Calculate the lengths of the sides marked with the letter x. Give your answers to 1 decimal place. 🖩

a)

b)

❷ Work out the length of the diagonal of this rectangle. 🖩

❸ A ship sets off from Port A and travels 50km due north, then 80km due east to reach Port B. How far is Port A from Port B by the shortest route? 🖩

Not to scale

Area of 2-D shapes

Perimeter and area of 2-D shapes — B2

The perimeter is the distance around the outside edge of a shape.

The area is the amount of space a 2-D shape covers.

Common units of area are square millimetres (mm^2), square centimetres (cm^2), square metres (m^2), etc.

Areas of quadrilaterals and triangles — B2

Area of a rectangle

Area = length × width
$A = l \times w$

Width (w)
Length (l)

Area of a parallelogram

Area = base × perpendicular height
$A = b \times h$
Remember to use the perpendicular height, not the slant height.

Perpendicular height (h)
Base (b)

Area of a triangle

Area = $\frac{1}{2}$ × base × perpendicular height
$A = \frac{1}{2} \times b \times h$

Perpendicular height (h)
Base (b)

Area of a trapezium

Area = $\frac{1}{2}$ × (sum of parallel sides) × perpendicular distance between them
$A = \frac{1}{2} \times (a + b) \times h$
or $A = \frac{(a + b)h}{2}$

a
Height (h)
b

You must learn all these formulae (except for the trapezium).

Examples

a) Find the areas of the following shapes.

i) $A = b \times h$
= 12×4
= $48cm^2$

5cm   4cm
12cm

ii) $A = \frac{1}{2} \times (a + b) \times h$
= $\frac{1}{2} \times (4 + 10) \times 6$
= 7×6
= $42cm^2$

10cm
4cm
6cm

b) The diagram opposite shows the plan of a floor.

i) Calculate the area of the floor.

3m   5m
6m   6m
4m

Split the shape into two parts:
Rectangle: $A = l \times w$
= 6×4
= $24m^2$

6m
4m

Triangle: $A = \frac{1}{2} \times b \times h$
= $\frac{1}{2} \times 4 \times 3$
= $6m^2$

5m
3m
4m

Total area of floor = 24 + 6 = $30m^2$

This could also be done using the trapezium formula.

ii) Skirting board is sold in 3m lengths. How many lengths are needed to go around the four walls of the room?

Perimeter of room = 3 + 6 + 4 + 6 + 5 = 24m
Skirting board = 3m lengths. 24 ÷ 3 = 8, so eight lengths of skirting board are needed.

Geometry and measures

Areas of enlargement and changing area units   B3

If a shape is enlarged by a **scale factor n**, then the **area** is n^2 times bigger. For example, if $n = 2$, the lengths are twice as big and the area is four times as big ($n^2 = 4$).

Area = 1cm²

Area = 4cm²

1cm $n = 2$ 2cm

It is always better to change units before you start a question in order to avoid possible errors.

This example will help you to change area units. The square has a length of 1m. This is the same as a length of 100cm.

1m   100cm

1m   100cm

Area = 1m²   Area = 10000cm²

Therefore $1m^2 = 10000cm^2$
(not $100cm^2$ as many people think!)

Circumference and area of a circle   B3

Circumference = π × diameter **or** $C = \pi d$
Circumference = π × 2 × radius **or** $C = 2\pi r$

Area = π × (radius)²
$A = \pi r^2$

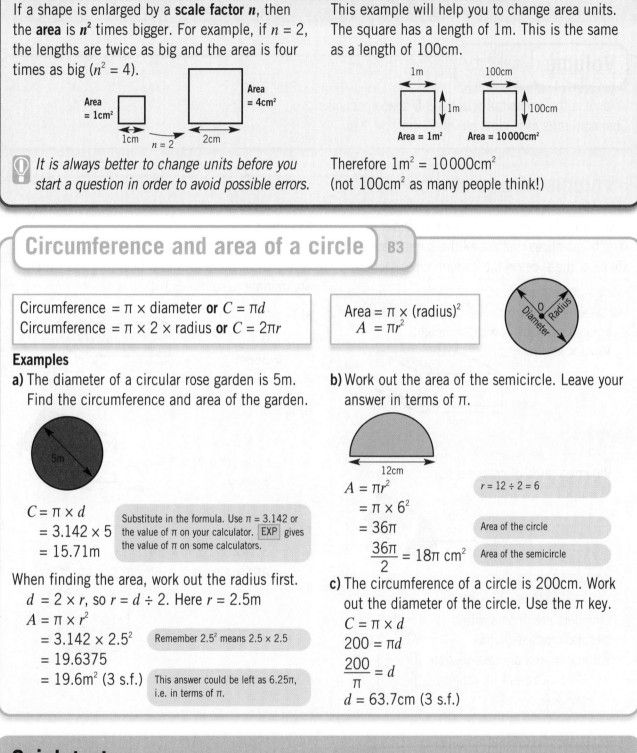

Examples

a) The diameter of a circular rose garden is 5m. Find the circumference and area of the garden.

5m

$C = \pi \times d$
$= 3.142 \times 5$
$= 15.71m$

Substitute in the formula. Use π = 3.142 or the value of π on your calculator. EXP gives the value of π on some calculators.

When finding the area, work out the radius first.
$d = 2 \times r$, so $r = d \div 2$. Here $r = 2.5m$
$A = \pi \times r^2$
$= 3.142 \times 2.5^2$ Remember 2.5^2 means 2.5×2.5
$= 19.6375$
$= 19.6m^2$ (3 s.f.)   This answer could be left as 6.25π, i.e. in terms of π.

b) Work out the area of the semicircle. Leave your answer in terms of π.

12cm

$A = \pi r^2$ $r = 12 \div 2 = 6$
$= \pi \times 6^2$
$= 36\pi$ Area of the circle
$\frac{36\pi}{2} = 18\pi \ cm^2$ Area of the semicircle

c) The circumference of a circle is 200cm. Work out the diameter of the circle. Use the π key.
$C = \pi \times d$
$200 = \pi d$
$\frac{200}{\pi} = d$
$d = 63.7cm$ (3 s.f.)

Quick test

1. Work out the areas of these shapes, giving your answers to 3 significant figures where appropriate.

a) 4cm   8cm   12cm

b) 5cm   12cm

c) 9cm

d) 8cm   15cm

2. Work out the area of the shaded region.

10cm   10cm

Volume of 3-D shapes

Volume `B2` `B3`

Volume is the amount of space a 3-D shape occupies.
Common units of volume are mm³, cm³, m³, etc.

Volume of prisms `B2` `B3`

A **prism** is any solid that can be cut across its
length into slices that are all the same shape. The
shape of the slices is the uniform cross-section.

Volume of a cuboid

Volume = length × width × height
$V = l \times w \times h$

Height

Width

Length

Volume of a prism

Volume = area of cross-section × length
$V = a \times l$

Area of
cross-section →

Length

Volume of a cylinder

Cylinders are prisms with
circular cross-sections.
Volume = area of cross-section
× height (or length)
$V = \pi r^2 \times h$

Radius

Height

Examples
Find the volume of the following 3-D shapes.
Give your answers to 3 significant figures, where
appropriate. Use π = 3.142

a) $V = l \times w \times h$
= 6 × 2 × 3
= 36cm³

3cm

2cm

6cm

b) $V = a \times l$
= ($\frac{1}{2}$ × b × h) × l
= ($\frac{1}{2}$ × 10 × 7) × 15
= 525cm³

7cm

15cm

10cm

c) $V = \pi r^2 \times h$
= 3.142 × 10.7² × 24.1
= 8669.43cm³
= 8670cm³

10.7cm

24.1cm

Converting volume units `B3`

The cube opposite has a length of 1m – this is the
same as a length of 100cm.
Therefore 1m³ = 100 × 100 × 100 = 1 000 000cm³.
Not quite what you may think!

💡 *Converting volume units is a tricky topic that usually
catches everybody out. Change all the lengths to the
same unit before starting a question.*

1m

1m   1m

Volume = 1m³

100cm

100cm   100cm

Volume = 1 000 000cm³

Surface area of prisms `B2` `B3`

You need to be able to find the surface area of different prisms.

Cuboid

To find the surface area (SA) of a cuboid, work out the area of each face and then add them together.

$$SA = 2hl + 2hw + 2lw$$

Cylinder

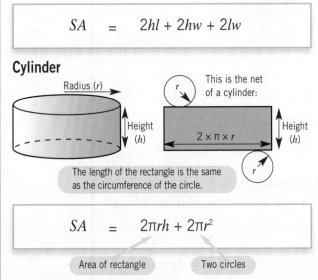

Radius (r)

This is the net of a cylinder:

$2 \times \pi \times r$

Height (h)

The length of the rectangle is the same as the circumference of the circle.

$$SA = 2\pi rh + 2\pi r^2$$

Area of rectangle — Two circles

Examples

a) Find the surface area of this cylinder. Use the π button. Give your answer to 1 decimal place.

$SA = 2 \times \pi \times 6 \times 10 + 2 \times \pi \times 6^2$
$\quad = 376.99... + 226.19...$
$\quad = 603.2\text{cm}^2$

6cm
10cm

b) A toy tent is shaped as a triangular prism. Work out the amount of material needed to make the tent.

8cm
10cm
20cm
6cm

❶ Draw a net of the triangular prism.

10cm
8cm   10cm
6cm
20cm   ① ② ③   20cm
8cm   10cm

❷ Work out the area of each face.
Triangles (× 2): $A = \frac{1}{2} \times b \times h$
$\quad\quad = \frac{1}{2} \times 6 \times 8$
$\quad\quad = 24\text{cm}^2 \times 2 = 48\text{cm}^2$

Rectangle ①: $A = l \times w$
$\quad\quad = 20 \times 8 = 160\text{cm}^2$

Rectangle ②: $A = l \times w$
$\quad\quad = 20 \times 6 = 120\text{cm}^2$

Rectangle ③: $A = l \times w$
$\quad\quad = 20 \times 10 = 200\text{cm}^2$

❸ Add them together.
Total amount of material needed
$= 48 + 160 + 120 + 200 = 528\text{cm}^2$

Volumes of enlargements `B3`

For an enlargement of **scale factor n**, the volumes are n^3 **times bigger**.

For example, if a cube of length 1cm is enlarged by a scale factor of 2:
$n = 2$, so $V = 2^3 = 8$ times bigger

1cm
1cm   1cm
Volume = 1cm³

2cm
2cm   2cm
Volume = 8cm³

Quick test

❶ Work out the volumes of these 3-D shapes. Give your answers to 3 significant figures.

a)

6.5cm
19.8cm
27.2cm

b)

85cm
10.6cm

❷ Work out the total surface area of the following triangular prism.

4cm
5cm
10cm
3cm

Practice questions

Use these questions to test your progress. Check your answers on page 96. You may wish to answer these questions on a separate piece of paper so that you can show full working out, which you will be expected to do in the exam.

1 Write down the readings on these scales. `B1` `B2`

a)

70   80

b)

11

110

2 Write these times using 24-hour clock time.
a) 7.42am   b) 6.13pm   c) 7.35pm   d) 3.09am

3 Richard needs to be at the train station by 1426. He leaves home at 1406. His journey to the train station takes 12 minutes. Will he get to the train station in time?

4 Jerry said, 'The distance between Manchester and London is 240 miles to the nearest whole mile.' Write down the shortest possible distance between Manchester and London.

5 Some angles are written on cards: `B2`

| 64° | 72° | 146° | 327° | 90° | 107° |

Which of these angles are...
a) acute?   b) obtuse?   c) reflex?   d) a right angle?

6 Calculate the sizes of the angles marked with letters.

35°

50°

a

a   b   c   d

a ....

b ....

c ....

d ....

7 Change 500g into pounds.

74

8 Work out the areas of these shapes.

a)

10m

12m

b)

12cm

8cm

6cm

9 James wants to turf his garden. The shape of the garden is shown. Turf costs £5 per square metre. You can only buy a whole number of square metres. How much will the turf cost for James' garden?

4m

6m

5m

9m

10 How many faces does a cuboid have?

11 A car travels a distance of 325 miles at an average speed of 65mph. How long does it take?

12 On a grid...

$\binom{3}{-2}$ translates shape A to shape B

$\binom{2}{4}$ translates shape B to shape C.

Write down the column vector that translates shape A directly to shape C.

13 The scale of a road map is 1 : 25000. Amersham and Watford are 30cm apart on the map. Work out the real distance in km between Amersham and Watford.

14 A ladder of length 6m rests so that the foot of the ladder is 3m away from a wall. Calculate how far up the wall the ladder reaches. Give your answer to 2 significant figures.

15 Calculate the volume of the oil drum, clearly stating your units. Use π = 3.142. Give your answer to 3 significant figures.

125cm

Express Oil

1.58m

B3

Geometry and measures

How well did you do?

0–3 **Try again**   4–7 **Getting there**   8–11 **Good work**   12–15 **Excellent!**

Probability 1

What is probability? B1

Probability is the chance or likelihood that something will happen. All probabilities lie from 0 to 1 inclusive.

An event with a probability of 0.62 is more likely to happen than an event with a probability of 0.6, since 0.62 is nearer to 1.

Exhaustive events account for all possible outcomes. For example, the list HH, HT, TH, TT gives all possible outcomes when two coins are tossed simultaneously.

Mutually exclusive events or outcomes cannot happen at the same time. For example, if a student is chosen at random:

Event A: the student is a girl
Event B: the student is a boy

These are **mutually exclusive** because no student can be both a boy and a girl.

Event C: the student has brown hair
Event D: the student wears glasses

These are **not mutually exclusive** because brown-haired students may wear glasses.

$$\text{Probability of an event} = \frac{\text{number of times the event can happen}}{\text{total number of possible outcomes}}$$

P(event) is a shortened way of writing the probability of an event.

Example
There are six blue, four yellow and two red beads in a bag. John chooses a bead at random. What is the probability he chooses...

a) a red bead?

$P(red) = \frac{2}{12}$ or $\frac{1}{6}$

b) a yellow bead?

$P(yellow) = \frac{4}{12}$ or $\frac{1}{3}$

c) a blue, yellow or red bead?

$P(blue, yellow or red) = \frac{12}{12} = 1$

d) a white bead?

$P(white) = 0$

Probabilities must be written as a fraction, decimal or percentage. Probabilities can never be negative or greater than 1.

Expected outcome B1

The expected outcome of an event is also known as theoretical probability.

Examples
a) A fair dice is thrown 300 times. Approximately how many fives are likely to be obtained?

There are six possible outcomes and all are equally likely.

$P(5) = \frac{1}{6} \times 300 = 50$ fives

Multiply 300 by $\frac{1}{6}$ since a 5 is expected $\frac{1}{6}$ of the time.

b) The probability of passing a driving test at the first attempt is 0.65. If there are 200 people taking their test for the first time, how many would you expect to pass?

$0.65 \times 200 = $
130 people would be expected to pass

Relative frequencies | B1

Relative frequencies are used to estimate probability. If it is not possible to calculate a probability, an experiment can be used to find the relative frequency.

Relative frequency of an event	=	number of times event occurred / total number of trials

Example

When a fair dice was thrown 80 times, a six came up 12 times. What is the relative frequency of getting a six?

Number of trials = 80
Number of sixes = 12
Relative frequency = $\frac{12}{80}$ = 0.15

Using experiments to calculate relative frequencies | B1

If a fair dice was thrown 180 times it would be expected that 30 twos would be thrown.

$\frac{1}{6} \times 180 = 30$

Example

Throw a dice 180 times and record the frequency of twos in every 30 throws.

Number of throws	Total frequency of twos	Relative frequency
30	3	0.1
60	7	0.12
90	16	0.18
120	19	0.16
150	24	0.16
180	31	0.17

It is expected that one-sixth ($\frac{1}{6}$ = 0.1$\dot{6}$ = 0.17) of the throws will be twos.

As the number of throws increases, the relative frequency gets closer to the expected probability.

The relative frequency is obtained by dividing the total frequency of twos by the number of throws, i.e. 16 ÷ 90

Quick test

1. Write down an event that will have a probability of zero.

2. A box contains three salt and vinegar, four cheese and two bacon-flavoured packets of crisps.
   If a packet of crisps is chosen at random, what is the probability that it is...
   a) salt and vinegar?   **b)** cheese?   **c)** onion flavoured?

3. The probability of achieving a grade C in mathematics is 0.48
   If 500 students sit the exam, how many would you expect to achieve a grade C?

4. When a fair dice was thrown 200 times, a five came up 47 times. What is the relative frequency of getting a five?

Probability 2

Possible outcomes of two or more events · B1

You can use lists, tables and sample space diagrams when answering probability questions with two **successive events**.

Lists · B1

Making a systematic list of possible outcomes of two events is useful.

Example

A coin is tossed twice. Make a list of the possible outcomes. What is the probability of getting two heads?

There are four different outcomes:

HH	TT	HT	TH
Both heads	Both tails	1st head, 2nd tail	1st tail, 2nd head

$P(HH) = \frac{1}{4}$

ⓘ *When there are two events, you need to show all the outcomes clearly – this will make calculating probabilities easier.*

Sample space diagrams · B1

A table is helpful when considering the outcomes of two events. This kind of table is sometimes known as a **sample space diagram**.

Example

Two dice are thrown together and their scores are added. Draw a diagram to show all the outcomes. Find the probability of...

a) a score of 7

$P(\text{score of 7}) = \frac{6}{36} = \frac{1}{6}$

b) a score that is a multiple of 4

$P(\text{multiple of 4}) = \frac{9}{36} = \frac{1}{4}$

c) a score of 2 or 3.

$P(\text{score of 2 or 3}) = \frac{3}{36} = \frac{1}{12}$

		First dice					
		1	2	3	4	5	6
Second dice	1	2	3	4	5	6	7
	2	3	4	5	6	7	8
	3	4	5	6	7	8	9
	4	5	6	7	8	9	10
	5	6	7	8	9	10	11
	6	7	8	9	10	11	12

There are 36 possible outcomes.

Example

The **two-way table** shows the number of students in a class who are left-handed or right-handed.

Hand	Male	Female	Total
Right	14	10	24
Left	2	7	9
Total	16	17	33

a) What is the probability that a person chosen at random is right-handed?

$$P(\text{right-handed}) = \frac{24}{33} = \frac{8}{11}$$

b) If a boy is chosen at random, what is the probability that he is left-handed?

$$P(\text{left-handed boy}) = \frac{2}{16} = \frac{1}{8}$$

See page 80 for more on two-way tables.

Probability of an event not happening   B1

If two events are **mutually exclusive**, then:

P(event will happen) = 1 – P(event will not happen)

or

P(event will not happen) = 1 – P(event will happen)

Examples

a) The probability that someone will get flu next winter is 0.42. What is the probability that they will not get flu next winter?

P(not get flu) = 1 – P(get flu)

= 1 – 0.42

= 0.58

b) Mrs Smith chooses one book from her library each week. She chooses a horror story, a thriller or a crime novel. The probability that she chooses a horror story is 0.35. The probability that she chooses a thriller is 0.25. Work out the probability that Mrs Smith chooses a crime novel.

Probability she chooses a horror story or thriller is 0.35 + 0.25 = 0.6

Probability she chooses a crime novel is
1 – P(does not choose a crime novel)

= 1 – 0.6

= 0.4

c) A bag contains only red, yellow and orange counters. Hannah is going to take a counter at random from the bag. A table is drawn to show the probability that Hannah will take a red, yellow or orange counter.

Colour	Red	Yellow	Orange
Probability	0.3	0.5	

i) Work out the probability that Hannah takes an orange counter.

P(orange counter) = 1 – P(not orange)

= 1 – (0.3 + 0.5)

= 1 – 0.8

= 0.2

ii) Hannah says that there are 12 yellow counters in the bag. Explain why she is wrong.

If there are 12 yellow counters, then since P(yellow) = 0.5 there must be 24 counters in total. However, 0.3 × 24 = 7.2, which is not a whole number of red counters, so Hannah must be wrong.

Quick test

1 The probability that it will not rain tomorrow is $\frac{2}{9}$. What is the probability that it will rain tomorrow?

2 a) Draw a sample space diagram that shows the possible outcomes when two dice are thrown together and their scores are multiplied.

b) What is the probability of getting a score of 6?

c) What is the probability of getting a score of 37?

Collecting data

Data collection B1

The census is one of the largest surveys, or data collection processes, that takes place. The census is done every 10 years and its main aim is to give a 'snapshot' of Britain at the time. In order to carry out the census, all households are given a survey to complete.

Types of data B1

There are two main types of data:

Quantitative
The answer is a number, e.g. How many blue cars are there in a car park?

Qualitative
The answer is a word, e.g. What is your favourite colour?

Quantitative data can be discrete or continuous:
• **Discrete data** has an exact value. Each category is separate and is usually found by counting. An example is the number of people with brown hair.

• **Continuous data** has values that merge from one category to the next. Examples include the heights and weights of students. Continuous data cannot be measured exactly. The accuracy of the measurement relies on the accuracy of the measuring equipment.

Primary data is data that is collected by the person who is going to analyse and use it.

Secondary data is data that is available from an external source, such as books, newspapers and the Internet.

Hypotheses and experiments B1

A hypothesis is a **prediction** that can be tested. Experiments can be used to test hypotheses.

For example:
Hypothesis: The better the light, the faster seedlings grow.
Variable: This is the intensity of the light, the condition that can be changed.

Conditions: The other conditions must stay the same. All seedlings must be exactly the same size, strength and colour to start with. If there is **bias** (e.g. if one side of the tray gets more water), then the experiment needs to start again.

Two-way tables B1

Data can be collected and displayed in a two-way table. This is a table in which data can be read horizontally and vertically.

For example, the table shows the results of a survey of the languages studied by students in a school.

	French	Spanish	German	Total
Female	16	9	1	26
Male	12	12	8	32
Total	28	21	9	58

Questionnaires B1

Questionnaires can be used to test hypotheses.

When designing questionnaires…
- decide what you need to find out: the **hypothesis**
- give instructions on how the questionnaire has to be filled in
- do not ask for information that is not needed (e.g. name)
- make the questions clear and concise
- keep the questionnaire short
- if people's opinions are needed, make sure the question is **unbiased**. An example of a biased question would be: 'Do you agree that a leisure centre should have a tennis court rather than a squash court?'
- allow for all possible answers. For example, if you were asking 'Which of these is your favourite colour?', add an option for 'other'

- include a time period if it is needed, for example, 'For how many hours do you play computer games each week?'.

💡 *When asked to design a questionnaire, always word the questions carefully. Try to avoid bias appearing in your questions.*

Data collection sheet B1

When collecting data, a data collection sheet is often used. For example, Tracey and David carried out a survey of the colour of cars that passed the gates of their school during a 30-minute interval. Their data collection sheet looked like this:

Colour of car	Tally	Frequency

Siân carried out a survey for the school library. She wanted to find out the type of books students were reading. Her data collection sheet looked like this:

Type of book	Tally	Frequency

Quick test

1. Richard and Tammy are carrying out a survey to find out what students' favourite foods are. Design a data collection sheet that they could use.

2. Design a questionnaire you could give to a friend in order to find out what they do in their spare time.

Representing data 1

Pictograms B1

A pictogram can be used to represent discrete data. Pictograms use identical symbols, where each symbol represents a certain number of items.

For example:

Manchester	○ ○ ◖
Luxor	○ ○ ○ ○ ○ ○
Melbourne	○ ◖

Key ○ = 2 hours of sunshine

The pictogram shows the number of hours of sunshine one day in July. From the pictogram, you can see that...
* Melbourne had the fewest hours of sunshine
* Luxor had 12 hours of sunshine
* Manchester had 5 hours of sunshine.

Bar charts B1

Bar charts have bars of equal width to represent the frequency of discrete data. The width of each bar must be the same.

The bar chart opposite shows the favourite drinks of some students. From the bar chart, you can see that...
* cola is the favourite drink
* milk is the least favourite drink
* three more students prefer water to lemonade
* 8 + 11 + 2 + 5 = 26 students took part in the survey.

Make sure the width of the bars is equal.

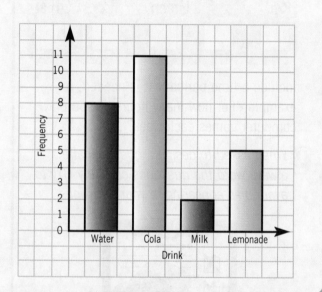

Line graphs B1

A line graph is a set of points joined by lines.

For example, the data below has been used to produce the line graph opposite.

Year	2005	2006	2007	2008	2009	2010
Number of cars sold	2500	2900	2100	1900	1600	800

Middle values, like point A, have no meaning. Point A does **not** show that halfway between 2007 and 2008, there were 2000 cars sold.

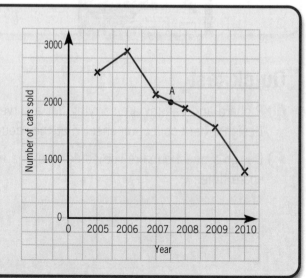

Dual and composite bar charts are used to compare data. Dual bar charts have the bars side by side, whereas composite bar charts have the bars on top of each other.

For example, Mr Morris, a PE teacher, wants to find out which sports his students prefer so that he can decide which sport to offer at the after-school club. The results of his survey are shown in the dual bar chart below.

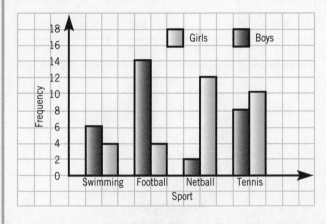

The same results are shown in the composite bar chart below.

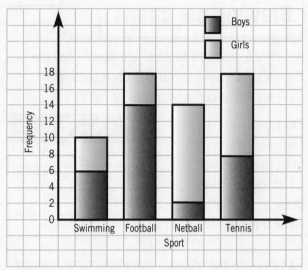

From the bar charts, you can see that…

- if an equal number of boys and girls attend the after-school club, Mr Morris should offer swimming and/or tennis
- if more boys attend the after-school club, Mr Morris should offer football
- if more girls attend the after-school club, Mr Morris should offer netball.

Quick test

1 The pictogram shows the number of letters sent to a business on four consecutive days.

Key: ✉ = 10 letters

a) How many letters arrived on Monday?

b) How many more letters arrived on Tuesday compared with Wednesday?

c) In total, 125 letters were received between Monday and Thursday. Complete the pictogram.

d) Explain why you think more letters arrived on the Monday.

Representing data 2

Drawing pie charts B1

Pie charts are used to illustrate data. They are circles split up into sections, each section representing a certain number of items.

Example
The table shows the favourite sports of 24 students in year 11. Draw a pie chart to show this data.

Sport	Frequency
Football	9
Swimming	5
Netball	3
Hockey	7
Total	24

To calculate the angles for the pie chart, follow these steps:
❶ Find the total for the items listed.
❷ Find the fraction of the total for each item.
❸ Multiply the fraction by 360° to find the angle.

Sport	Frequency	Angle	Workings
Football	9	135°	$\frac{9}{24} \times 360°$
Swimming	5	75°	$\frac{5}{24} \times 360°$
Netball	3	45°	$\frac{3}{24} \times 360°$
Hockey	7	105°	$\frac{7}{24} \times 360°$
Total	24	360°	

Interpreting pie charts B1

When the total number of items is known, the number of items in each category can be found.

Example
The pie chart shows how 18 students travel to school.

How many students travel by...
a) car? 360° = 18 students

$$1° = \frac{18}{360°} = 0.05$$
Work out what 1° represents.

60° × 0.05 = 3 students
b) bus? 80° × 0.05 = 4 students
c) foot? 220° × 0.05 = 11 students

💡 *Pie chart questions are usually worth about 4 marks at GCSE. Make sure the angles add up to 360° before drawing a pie chart. Measure the angles carefully since you are allowed only a 2° tolerance.*

Comparing pie charts B1

Pie charts can also be used to compare information.

Example
Jackie is an editor for two magazines. She wants to publish an article on a recently-formed boy band. The pie charts below show the age profile (in years) of the readers of both magazines.

After looking at the pie charts, Jackie decides to insert the article in Daisy Weekly because the 0–29 age group is bigger, so there are more younger readers. Explain why Jackie's decision might not be correct.

Jackie might not be correct because the data does not show how many readers there are in total for each magazine. For example, if Poppy Daily had 400 readers and Daisy Weekly had 90 readers, then 100 people in the 0–29 age group would read Poppy Daily, compared with only 30 people in the same age group reading Daisy Weekly.

Histograms B1

Histograms illustrate **continuous data**. They are similar to bar charts except that there are no gaps between the bars. The data must be grouped into equal **class intervals** if the length (height) of the bar is used to represent the frequency.

For example, the masses of 30 workers in a factory are shown in the table opposite.

$45 \leqslant W < 55$, etc. is called a class interval. In this example the class intervals are all equal in width. $45 \leqslant W < 55$ means the masses are at least 45kg but less than 55kg. A mass of 55kg would be in the next class interval.

Remember these points about histograms:
- The axes do not need to start at zero.
- The axes are labelled.
- The graph has a title.

Mass (W kg)	Frequency
$45 \leqslant W < 55$	7
$55 \leqslant W < 65$	13
$65 \leqslant W < 75$	6
$75 \leqslant W < 85$	4

Histogram showing masses of factory workers

Indicates that the x-axis does not start at 0.

Frequency polygons B1

To draw a frequency polygon, join the **midpoints** of **class intervals** for grouped or continuous data.

Consider the histogram of the factory workers again. To draw a frequency polygon, put a cross at the middle of the top of each bar and join up the crosses with a ruler, as shown opposite. Make sure the frequency polygon is labelled.

Histogram showing masses of factory workers

Frequency polygon

Quick test

1 Draw a pie chart for the data about hair colour opposite. 📱

2 a) Use the histogram to complete the frequency table opposite.
   b) How many students were in the survey?
   c) Draw a frequency polygon on the histogram.

Hair colour	Brown	Auburn	Blonde	Black
Frequency	8	4	6	6

Height (h cm)	Frequency
$140 \leqslant h < 145$	
$145 \leqslant h < 150$	10
$150 \leqslant h < 155$	
$155 \leqslant h < 160$	
$160 \leqslant h < 165$	

Histogram showing heights of year 10 students

Scatter diagrams & correlation

Scatter diagrams B1

A scatter diagram (scatter graph or scatter plot) is used to show two sets of data at the same time.

Its importance is to show the correlation (connection), if any, between two sets of data.

Types of correlation B1

There are three types of correlation:

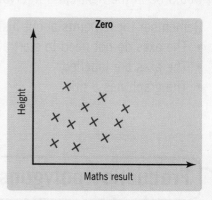

Positive correlation
Both variables are increasing. If the points are nearly in a straight line there is a strong positive correlation.

Negative correlation
One variable increases as the other decreases. If the points are nearly in a straight line there is a strong negative correlation.

Zero/no correlation
There is little or no linear relationship between the variables.

Drawing a scatter diagram B1

When drawing a scatter diagram...
- work out the scales first
- plot the points carefully
- each time a point is plotted, tick it off your list of data.

For example, the table shows the maths and history test results of 11 pupils.

Maths test (%)	76	79	38	42	49	75	83	82	66	61	54
History test (%)	70	36	84	70	74	42	29	33	50	56	64

Scatter diagram showing maths and history marks

The scatter diagram shows that there is a strong negative correlation – in general, the better the pupils did in maths, the worse they did in history, and vice versa.

The **line of best fit** is the line that best fits the data points on the scatter diagram. It goes in the direction of the data and there is roughly the same number of points above the line as below it. A line of best fit can be used to make predictions.

For example, if Hassam was away for the maths test but got 78% in the history test, then from the scatter diagram you can estimate that he would have got approximately 43% in maths.

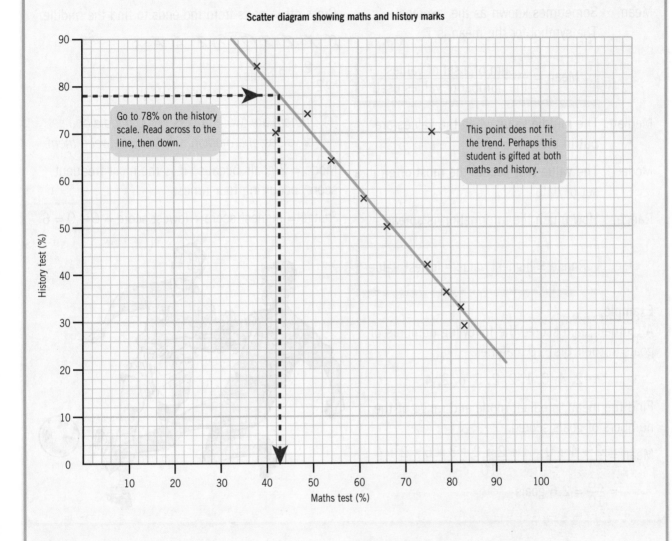

Scatter diagram showing maths and history marks

Go to 78% on the history scale. Read across to the line, then down.

This point does not fit the trend. Perhaps this student is gifted at both maths and history.

History test (%)

Maths test (%)

It is not wise to use the line of best fit outside the group of plotted points. For example, a person who got 5% in the history test would not get 106% for maths!

Do not rush when drawing a scatter diagram. Plot the points very carefully. Remember to show on your graph how you made your estimates.

Quick test

1 Write down what type of correlation you would expect for each pair of variables.
   a) The number of pages in a magazine and the number of advertisements.
   b) The heights of students in a year group and their marks in a maths test.
   c) The height up a mountain and the temperature.
   d) The age of a used car and its value.

Averages 1

Averages of discrete data B1

You should know three types of average: mean, median and mode.

Mean: Sometimes known as the 'average'. The symbol for the mean is $\bar{x}$.

$$\text{Mean} = \frac{\text{sum of a set of values}}{\text{the number of values used}}$$

Median: The **middle value** when the values are put in order of size.

Mode: The value that occurs the **most often** in a set of data.

Range: How much the information is **spread**.

$$\text{Range} = \text{highest value} - \text{lowest value}$$

Example
A football team scored the following numbers of goals in their first 10 matches.

2, 4, 0, 1, 2, 2, 3, 6, 2, 4

Find the mean, median, mode and range of the numbers of goals scored.

$$\text{Mean} = \frac{2 + 4 + 0 + 1 + 2 + 2 + 3 + 6 + 2 + 4}{10}$$

$$= \frac{26}{10} = 2.6 \text{ goals}$$

Median: put the data in order of size =
0, 1, 2, 2, 2, 2, 3, 4, 4, 6

Cross off in pairs from the ends to find the middle.

0̸ 1̸ 2̸ 2̸ ②② 3̸ 4̸ 4̸ 6̸

$$\frac{2 + 2}{2} = 2 \text{ goals}$$

If there are two numbers in the middle of a set of values, the median is halfway between them.

Mode = 2 goals because it is the most frequent score, occurring four times.

Range = highest score – lowest score = 6 – 0 = 6

Finding a missing value when given the mean B1

If you are given the mean of a set of discrete data, you can use the information to calculate a missing value.

Example
A manufacturer produces boxes of matches. He wishes to make the claim, 'Average of 48 matches per box'. In three out of the first four boxes he looks at, the number of matches is 45, 44 and 51. How many matches need to be in the fourth box in order for the manufacturer to make his claim?

Call the number of matches in the fourth box, y.

$$\frac{45 + 44 + 51 + y}{4} = 48$$

$$\frac{140 + y}{4} = 48$$

The mean number of matches must be 48.

$$140 + y = 48 \times 4$$
$$140 + y = 192$$
$$y = 52$$

He needs 52 matches in the fourth box in order to make his claim.

Finding averages from a frequency table B1

A frequency table tells you how many data items there are in a group. For example:

Number of sisters (x)	0	1	2	3	4
Frequency (f)	4	9	3	5	2

This means 2 people had 4 sisters.

Mean: $(\bar{x}) = \dfrac{\sum fx}{\sum f}$ ($\sum$ means 'the sum of')

$$= \frac{(4 \times 0) + (9 \times 1) + (3 \times 2) + (5 \times 3) + (2 \times 4)}{4 + 9 + 3 + 5 + 2}$$

$$= \frac{38}{23} = 1.7 \text{ (1 d.p.)}$$

💡 *When finding the mean from a frequency table, remember to divide by the sum of the frequencies and not by how many groups there are.*

Median: Since there are 23 people who have been asked, the median will be the 12th person in the table.

11 people	12th person	11 people

The 12th person has 1 sister ∴ the median = 1

Mode: This is the data value with the highest frequency, that is 1 sister.

Range: 4 – 0 = 4   Highest number of sisters – lowest number of sisters

Example

The table gives information on the number of minutes taken by different people to solve a problem.

Number of minutes (x)	0	1	2	3	4	5
Frequency (f)	1	5	6	10	3	1

Find the mean, median, mode and range of the number of minutes taken to solve the problem.

Mean: $(\bar{x}) = \dfrac{\sum fx}{\sum f}$

$$= \frac{(1 \times 0) + (5 \times 1) + (6 \times 2) + (10 \times 3) + (3 \times 4) + (1 \times 5)}{1 + 5 + 6 + 10 + 3 + 1}$$

$$= \frac{0 + 5 + 12 + 30 + 12 + 5}{26}$$

$$= \frac{64}{26}$$

$$= 2.46 \text{ minutes (2 d.p.)}$$

Median: Since there are 26 people who solved the problem, the median is between the 13th and 14th person, who both took 3 minutes.

12 people	13th/14th person	12 people

∴ the median = 3 minutes

Mode: 3 minutes, as this is the value with the highest frequency.

Range: 5 – 0 = 5 minutes

Quick test

1 Find the mean, median, mode and range of this set of data. 🖩
2, 9, 3, 6, 4, 4, 5, 8, 4

2 Charlotte made this table to show the number of minutes students were late for registration.

Number of minutes late (x)	0	1	2	3	4
Frequency (f)	10	4	6	3	2

Calculate... 🖩
a) the mean   b) the median   c) the mode   d) the range.

Averages 2

Averages of grouped data B1

When data values are grouped into class intervals, the exact data values are not known. You can estimate the mean by using the **midpoint** of the **class interval**. The midpoint is the halfway value.

When you are using grouped (continuous) data, you can only find the modal class as opposed to the mode. This is the class interval with the highest frequency.

💡 *Finding the mean of grouped data is a very common GCSE question and is usually worth about 4 marks.*

For example, the table below shows the masses of some year 9 students.

Mass (W kg)	Frequency (f)	Midpoint (x)	fx
40 ≤ W < 45	7	42.5	297.5
45 ≤ W < 50	4	47.5	190
50 ≤ W < 55	3	52.5	157.5
55 ≤ W < 60	1	57.5	57.5

Adding these extra columns helps to show your working out.

$$\text{Mean} = \frac{\Sigma fx}{\Sigma f}$$

$$= \frac{(7 \times 42.5) + (4 \times 47.5) + (3 \times 52.5) + (1 \times 57.5)}{7 + 4 + 3 + 1}$$

$$= \frac{702.5}{15} = 46.8 \text{kg (1 d.p.)}$$

This method is the same as on page 89 except that the frequency is multiplied by the **midpoint of each class interval**.

The **modal class** is $40 \leq W < 45$.

Median
How to find the class interval containing the median:
$$\frac{(15 + 1)}{2} = 8$$

The median is therefore the eighth year 9 student.

Mass (W kg)	Frequency	
40 ≤ W < 45	7	1st to 7th student
45 ≤ W < 50	4	8th to 11th student

The median lies in the class interval $45 \leq W < 50$.

💡 *If your calculator will do statistical calculations, learn how to use these functions. It is much quicker but always do it twice as a check. Always try to show full working out in order to obtain some method marks.*

Using appropriate averages B1

Choosing which average to use depends on the type of data you have and what you are looking for in it:
- The **mean** is useful when you need a 'typical' value. Be careful not to use the mean if there are extreme values.
- The **median** is a useful average if there are extreme values.
- The **mode** is useful when you need the most common value.

Stem-and-leaf diagrams B1

Stem-and-leaf diagrams are used for recording and displaying information. They can also be used to find the mode, median and range of a set of data.

For example, these are the marks gained by some students in a mathematics exam:

24   61   55   36   42

32   60   51   38   58

55   52   47   55   55

When the information is put into a stem-and-leaf diagram it looks like this:

```
Stem │ Leaf
  2  │ 4                Stem is 30, leaf is 2 ∴ 32
  3  │ 2   6   8
  4  │ 2   7
  5  │ 1   2   5   5   5   5   8
  6  │ 0   1            Key: 4 │ 2 = 42 marks
```

To read off the values you multiply the stem by 10 and add on the leaf.

Using the stem-and-leaf diagram, the mode, median and range can be found easily.

Mode   = 55
Median = 52
Range = 61 – 24 = 37

Back-to-back stem-and-leaf diagrams are particularly useful when comparing two sets of data. This back-to-back stem-and-leaf diagram shows the times, to the nearest minute, taken by some students to complete a logic problem.

Boys' times		Girls' times
7 7 5 4 0	1	2 5 5 7
6 6 3 1 1	2	3 8 8 9
8 7	3	0 1 2 3 9
9 7 5	4	2 3

Key for boys' times: 7 │ 1 = 17 minutes
Key for girls' times: 1 │ 5 = 15 minutes

Using averages and spread to compare distributions B1

Be careful when drawing conclusions from averages, as they do not always tell the whole story.

For example, the lifetime of two types of battery is tested. The mean lifetime of Trojan batteries is 9.2 hours. The mean lifetime of Warrior batteries is 11.6 hours.

From the averages, you might say that all Warrior batteries last longer than Trojan batteries. However, if you look at the range for each type of battery, you can see that this is not true:

Range of Trojan battery = 14.6 hours – 5.8 hours
                        = 8.8 hours

Range of Warrior battery = 13.2 hours – 9.3 hours
                        = 3.9 hours

Using the range, you can see that not all Warrior batteries last longer than Trojan batteries. The average lifetime of the Trojan batteries has been reduced because some of them have a particularly low lifetime.

Quick test

1. The heights of some year 10 pupils are shown in the table.

Height (h cm)	$140 \leqslant h < 145$	$145 \leqslant h < 150$	$150 \leqslant h < 155$	$155 \leqslant h < 160$	$160 \leqslant h < 165$
Frequency	4	7	14	5	2

   a) Calculate an estimate for the mean of this data. Give your answer to 2 decimal places. 🖩
   b) Write down the modal class.
   c) Write down the class interval that contains the median.

Practice questions

Use these questions to test your progress. Check your answers on page 96. You may wish to answer these questions on a separate piece of paper so that you can show full working out, which you will be expected to do in the exam.

1 A bag contains three red, four blue and six green balls. If a ball is chosen at random from the bag, what is the probability of choosing…

a) a red ball?   **b)** a green ball?   **c)** a yellow ball?   **d)** a blue or a red ball?

(B1)

2 The probability that Josie gets full marks in a tables test is 0.82
What is the probability that she does not get full marks in a tables test?

3 The probability of passing a driving test is 0.7
If 200 people take the test today, how many would you expect to pass?

4 Two spinners are used in a game. The first spinner is labelled 2, 4, 6, 8.
The second spinner is labelled 3, 5, 5, 7. Both spinners are spun.
The score is found by multiplying the numbers on each spinner.

a) Complete the table to show the possible scores.

b) What is the probability of getting an even score?

c) What is the probability of getting a score of 10?

Second spinner	First spinner			
	2	4	6	8
3				
5				
5				
7				

5 This pictogram has no key. The pictogram shows the number of cups of tea Mrs Bassett sold in her tea shop during one week. She sold 25 cups of tea on Wednesday.

Day	
Sunday	
Monday	◯ ◯ ◯ ◖
Tuesday	◯ ◯
Wednesday	◯ ◯ ◖
Thursday	◯ ◯ ◖
Friday	◯ ◯ ◯ ◯ ◖
Saturday	◯

a) How many cups of tea did Mrs Bassett sell during the week?

b) William says, 'Nobody wanted a cup of tea on Sunday because the weather was too hot.' Give another reason why no cups of tea were sold on Sunday.

6 Reece carried out a survey to find out the favourite flavours of crisps of students in his year. The results are shown in the table (right). Draw a pie chart of this information. 🖩

Crisp flavour	Number of students
Cheese and onion	14
Salt and vinegar	20
Beef	12
Smoky bacon	2

7 A youth club has 75 members, of which 42 are boys. There are 15 members who are boys under 13 years old. There are 21 members who are girls aged 13 and over.

a) Complete the two-way table. 🖩

b) How many of the girls are under 13 years old?

	Under 13 years old	13 years old and over	Total
Boys			
Girls			
Total			

8 Katie has to choose someone to enter a spelling contest. The last 10 scores (out of 10) for Lucy and Rashna are given below:

Lucy: 5, 6, 8, 4, 1, 1, 3, 10, 2, 10
Rashna: 6, 6, 5, 5, 4, 4, 5, 5, 6, 4

a) Work out the mean scores and ranges for Lucy and Rashna. 🖩

b) Who should Katie choose to be in the spelling contest and why?

9 The daily number of guests in a hotel over a two-week period was recorded.

42   38   27   52   37   56   25
57   28   44   50   39   38   46

a) Draw an ordered stem-and-leaf diagram of this data.

b) Use your stem-and-leaf diagram to find...

i) the mode

ii) the range.

c) Emma says, 'On three days, there were fewer than 30 guests.' Is Emma correct?

10 Jonathan is doing a survey into whether people play sport. He decides to ask 50 people by standing outside a sports centre on a Wednesday morning. Explain why his survey will be biased.

Statistics and probability

How well did you do?

| 0–3 | Try again | 4–5 | Getting there | 6–8 | Good work | 9–10 | Excellent! |

Answers

Number   Quick test answers

Page 5   Types of numbers
1. 11, 13, 17, 19, 23, 29   **2.** HCF: 12; LCM: 120
3. a) ±8   b) 6   **4.** a) $\frac{4}{3}$ b) $\frac{p}{x}$ c) $\frac{1}{5}$ d) 10

Page 7   Positive & negative numbers
1. 3°C   **2.** a) 4   b) -16   c) -12   d) -12   e) 5   f) 6   g) 7   h) -10   i) 36

Page 9   Working with numbers
1. a) 1177   b) 232   c) 1722   d) 275
2. 20496   **3.** 37
4. a) 164   b) 890   c) 37000   d) 0.097
5. 42 people

Page 11   Fractions
1. a) $\frac{1}{3}$ b) $\frac{7}{20}$ c) $\frac{6}{13}$ d) $1\frac{1}{3}$ e) $\frac{5}{21}$ f) $\frac{4}{21}$ g) $\frac{49}{121}$ h) $\frac{50}{63}$
2. £40   **3.** 247mm   **4.** $\frac{4}{15}$

Page 13   Decimals
1. a) 36.48   b) 17.679   c) 26.88   d) 12.3   e) 6   f) 52
   g) 0.4   h) 0.0037   i) 4000   j) 45000   k) 470000   l) 32500
   m) 693   n) 291   o) 7.074   p) 0.0284
2. a) 2.607, 2.61, 2.615, 4.02, 4.021, 4.20
   b) 6.05, 6.49, 8.206, 8.27, 8.271, 8.93

Page 15   Rounding
1. a) 6.43   b) 18.61   c) 14.27   d) 29.64
2. a) 2800   b) 270   c) 39000   d) 0.027
3. 6700km

Page 17   Indices
1. a) 12^{12} b) 9^6 c) 4   d) 18^4 e) 4^9 f) 1
2. a) x^{13} b) $6x^{16}$ c) $4x^2$ d) $5x^7$ e) $2x^{12}$ f) $16x^{10}$

Page 19   Percentages 1
1. £210   **2.** 74.6%   **3.** 9.9lb   **4.** Super's; £33.33

Page 21   Percentages 2
1. £161.50   **2.** a) £1800   b) £6180   **3.** £3392

Page 22   Fractions, decimals & percentages
1. a) i) 0.2857   ii) 0.6   iii) 0.8̇
   b) i) 28.57%   ii) 60%   iii) 88.8̇%
2. 0.041, 5%, 26%, $\frac{1}{3}$, $\frac{2}{5}$, 0.42

Page 23   Using a calculator
1. a) 14.45   b) 769.6   c) 7.052   d) $8\frac{1}{3}$ or 8.3̇

Page 25   Approximations & checking calculations
1. 100   **2.** 10 rolls   **3.** £7.45 (check: £175 ÷ 25 = £7✓)

Page 27   Ratio
1. a) 4 : 5   b) 1 : 2   c) 5 : 2
2. 10, 15 and 35 sweets respectively   **3.** £2.76   **4.** 36cm

Pages 28–29   Answers to practice questions
1. The 100ml tube of toothpaste, since 50ml costs 2.48p per ml, 75ml
   costs 2.61p per ml and 100ml costs 2.42p per ml.
2. 5.032, 5.04, 5.42, 6.27, 6.385, 6.39
3. a) 625g sugar   b) 750g self-raising flour   **4.** £25000
5. £799.20   **6.** a) 365   b) 0.706   **7.** £315
8. a) 9, 21, 41   b) 9, 64, 100   c) 2, 41   d) 2, 40   e) 40, 64, 100
9. 9°C   **10.** £44764   **11.** £27
12. a) 56   b) 508   c) 7002
13. Six million, four hundred and fifty seven thousand, two hundred and
    seventy-nine
14. $\frac{9+9}{0.2 \times 50} = \frac{18}{10} = 1.8$
15. a) $2^3 \times 3^2 = 8 \times 9 = 72$ b) a^7 c) b^4 d) $\frac{16a^3}{4a^2} = 4a^7$ e) a^{20}
16. 1.5cm   **17.** 77.3̇%   **18.** £440.63

Algebra   Quick test answers

Page 31   Algebra
1. a) $10a$ b) $8a + b$ c) $9x + 4y$ d) $4x^2y - 5xy^2$
2. a) $3x + 6$ b) $2x + 2y$ c) $-6x - 12$ d) $8x + 13$ e) $7x + 8$
   f) $10x + 12$
3. a) $2(2x^2 + 1)$ b) $2(y - 2)$ c) $2(3x + 5)$ d) $3x(x + 3)$
   e) $5x(3 - 4x)$ f) $x(x - 5)$

Page 33   Equations 1
1. a) $x = 4$ b) $x = 6$ c) $x = 20$ d) $x = 13$ e) $x = 24$ f) $x = 4.5$
   g) $x = 2$ h) $x = 4$ i) $x = -1$ j) $x = -1.4$

Page 35   Equations 2 & coordinates
1. 3.3
2. a) $4(x + 1) = 4x + 4$ b) $x = 9$ ∴ length = 11cm
3. A (3, 2); B (1, 4); C (-2, 1); D (-5, 0); E (-3, -4); F (2, -2)

Page 37   Patterns, sequences & inequalities
1. a) 13, 15   b) 25, 36   c) 4, 2
2. a) $2n + 3$ b) $3n - 1$ c) $4n + 2$ d) $10 - 2n$
3. a) $x < 6$ b) $x \geqslant 4$ c) $1 \leqslant x \leqslant 3$ d) $\frac{-1}{5} \leqslant x < 2$

Page 39   Formulae
1. a) 10   b) 14   c) 8   d) 6   e) -26
2. $b = \frac{a+d}{5}$ **3.** $m = \frac{y-c}{x}$ **4.** $R = \frac{V}{I}$

Page 41   Straight-line graphs
1. a) $x = 1$ b) $x = 1.5$
2. a) Gradient 2, intercept (0, 4)   b) Gradient 3, intercept (0, -2)
   c) Gradient 5, intercept (0, -4)

Page 43   Quadratic graphs
1. a)

x	-3	-2	-1	0	1	2	3
y	12	7	4	3	4	7	12

b)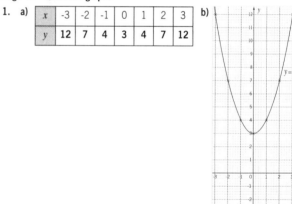

$y = x^2 + 3$

c) $x = -2.2$ and 2.2 approximately

2.

x	-3	-2	-1	0	1	2	3
y	17	7	1	-1	1	7	17

$y = 2x^2 - 1$

Page 45 Interpreting graphs
1. Container A, graph 3; container B, graph 1; container C, graph 2
2. a) 66.6̇mph b) 1 hour c) 50mph d) About 1442

Pages 46–47 Answers to practice questions
1. a)
   b)

Pattern number (p)	Number of matchsticks (m)
1	4
2	7
3	10
4	**13**
5	**16**
6	**19**

   c) 301 matchsticks   d) $m = 3p + 1$
2. 21, 25 3. $4n - 1$
4. a)

x	-2	-1	0	1	2	3
$y = 3x - 4$	**-10**	**-7**	-4	-1	**2**	**5**

   b)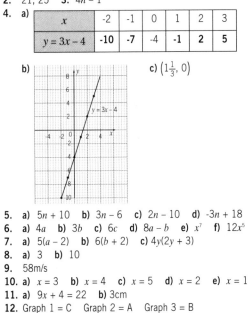
   c) $\left(1\frac{1}{3}, 0\right)$

5. a) $5n + 10$ b) $3n - 6$ c) $2n - 10$ d) $-3n + 18$
6. a) $4a$ b) $3b$ c) $6c$ d) $8a - b$ e) x^7 f) $12x^5$
7. a) $5(a - 2)$ b) $6(b + 2)$ c) $4y(2y + 3)$
8. a) 3 b) 10
9. 58m/s
10. a) $x = 3$ b) $x = 4$ c) $x = 5$ d) $x = 2$ e) $x = 1$
11. a) $9x + 4 = 22$ b) 3cm
12. Graph 1 = C   Graph 2 = A   Graph 3 = B
13. $T = 85y + 8z$
14. 1.8 15. $1 \leqslant n \leqslant 3$

Geometry and measures   Quick test answers
Page 49 Shapes
1. Hexagon 2. See information on pages 48–49.

Page 51 Solids
1.

2.

Plan	View from A (front elevation)	Side elevation B

Page 53 Angles
1. a) $a = 150°$ b) $b = 70°, c = 110°, d = 70°$
   c) $a = 50°, b = 50°, c = 130°, d = 50°$
2. a) $72°$ b) $108°$

Page 55 Bearings & scale drawings
1. a) $072°$ b) $305°$ c) $145°$
2. a) $252°$ b) $125°$ c) $325°$
3. 7km

Page 57 Constructions
1.   2.

Page 58 Symmetry
1.   2. a)   b)

3. Order 2

Page 59 Loci
1.

Page 61 Transformations 1
1. a)–d)

2. Move 2 to the left, 3 upwards 3. $\binom{-5}{11}$

Page 63 Transformations 2
1.   2. a)–b)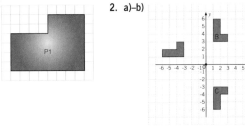

Page 65 Measures & measurement 1
1. 3.5kg 2. 6.6lb 3. 14 pints
4. a) 9.2 b) 9.5 c) 2.42 d) 2.46 e) 2.48 f) 6.25 g) 6.75
5. C (3kg)

Page 67 Measures & measurement 2
1. Lower limit = 9.15 secs
   Upper limit = 9.25 secs
2. Lower limit = 57.5kg
   Upper limit = 58.5kg
3. 3mph
4. 3.5 hours (or 3 hours 30 minutes)

Page 69 Pythagoras' theorem
1. a) 17.2cm b) 20.0cm 2. 17cm 3. 94.3km

Page 71 Area of 2-D shapes
1. a) 64cm² b) 60cm² c) 63.6cm² d) 208cm²
2. 21.5cm² (3 s.f.)

Page 73 Volume of 3-D shapes
1. a) 1750cm³ b) 60 100cm³
2. 132cm²

Answers

Pages 74–75 Answers to practice questions
1. **a)** 74 **b)** 10.75
2. **a)** 0742 **b)** 1813 **c)** 1935 **d)** 0309
3. Yes, by 8 minutes
4. 239.5 miles
5. **a)** 64°, 72° **b)** 146°, 107° **c)** 327° **d)** 90°
6. $a = 80°$, $b = 50°$, $c = 130°$, $d = 15°$
7. 1.1lb
8. **a)** 120m² **b)** 60cm²
9. £420
10. 6 faces
11. 5hrs
12. $\binom{5}{2}$
13. 7.5km
14. 5.2m
15. 1 940 000cm³ (= 1940 litres)

Statistics and probability Quick test answers
Page 77 Probability 1
1. **Any sensible answer, e.g.:** I will get a 7 when I throw a dice; I will get a 4 when I toss a coin.
2. **a)** $\frac{3}{9} = \frac{1}{3}$ **b)** $\frac{4}{9}$ **c)** 0
3. 240 students
4. $\frac{47}{200}$ (= 0.235)

Page 79 Probability 2
1. $\frac{7}{9}$
2. **a)**

		First dice				
		1	2	3	4	5	6
	1	1	2	3	4	5	6
Second	2	2	4	6	8	10	12
dice	3	3	6	9	12	15	18
	4	4	8	12	16	20	24
	5	5	10	15	20	25	30
	6	6	12	18	24	30	36

b) $\frac{4}{36} = \frac{1}{9}$ **c)** 0

Page 81 Collecting data
1.

Favourite food type	Tally	Frequency

2. Make sure your questionnaire follows the guidance given on page 81.

Page 83 Representing data 1
1. **a)** 50 letters
   b) 5 letters
   c) Thursday ✉ ✉ ✉
   d) Since there is no post on a Sunday and limited post on a Saturday, there can be a build-up of mail.

Page 85 Representing data 2
1. The angles for the pie chart are: Brown 120°, Auburn 60°, Blonde 90°, Black 90°
2. **a)** The frequencies for the heights are: $140 \leqslant h < 145 = 6$, $145 \leqslant h < 150 = 10$, $150 \leqslant h < 155 = 11$, $155 \leqslant h < 160 = 5$, $160 \leqslant h < 165 = 2$
   b) 34 students
   c) The frequency polygon should be plotted at the midpoints of the bars.

Page 87 Scatter diagrams & correlation
1. **a)** Positive **b)** Zero/no correlation **c)** Negative **d)** Negative

Page 89 Averages 1
1. Mean = 5; median = 4; mode = 4; range = 7
2. **a)** 1.32 mins **b)** 1 min **c)** 0 mins **d)** 4 mins

Page 91 Averages 2
1. **a)** 151.56cm **b)** $150 \leqslant h < 155$ **c)** $150 \leqslant h < 155$

Pages 92–93 Answers to practice questions
1. **a)** $\frac{3}{13}$ **b)** $\frac{6}{13}$ **c)** 0 **d)** $\frac{7}{13}$
2. 0.18
3. 140 people
4. **a)**

		First spinner			
		2	4	6	8
Second spinner	3	6	12	18	24
	5	10	20	30	40
	5	10	20	30	40
	7	14	28	42	56

b) $\frac{16}{16} = 1$ **c)** $\frac{2}{16} = \frac{1}{8}$
5. **a)** 160 cups of tea **b)** The tea shop was closed.
6.

Crisp flavour	Number of students	Angle
Cheese and onion	14	105°
Salt and vinegar	20	150°
Beef	12	90°
Smoky bacon	2	15°

7. **a)**

	Under 13 years old	13 years old and over	Total
Boys	15	27	42
Girls	12	21	33
Total	27	48	75

b) 12 girls
8. **a)** Lucy: mean = 5 and range = 9; Rashna: mean = 5 and range = 2
   b) Rashna. The mean scores are the same but Rashna is much more consistent as she has the smaller range.
9. **a)**

2	5 7 8
3	7 8 8 9
4	2 4 6
5	0 2 6 7

Key: 3 | 7 = 37

   b) i) 38 **ii)** 32
   c) Emma is correct. There were fewer than 30 guests on only three days.
10. People who visit a sports centre usually play sport. In addition, doing the survey on a Wednesday morning could mean that people who work do not get asked.

Answers